The Commonsense Guide to
Everyday Poisons

The Commonsense Guide to
Everyday Poisons

How to live with the products you love
(and what to do when accidents happen)

Teddy Vincent Angert, BSN, CSPI

Illustrations by Pablo Martinez

Printed in the United States of America

First Printing, 2018

ISBN 978-0692196120

destroying angel press
Portland, OR 97219

www.everydaypoisons.com

This book is dedicated to all the hardworking SPIs, CSPIs and PIPs who spend their days and nights answering phones, solving problems and saving lives, and most especially to the staff of the Oregon Poison Center.

May all your exposures be silica gels!

Contents

What are Everyday Poisons?

All things are poison and nothing is without poison.
Only the dose makes a thing not a poison.

- Paracelsus

You live with a killer!

Dihydrogen monoxide (DHMO), also known as hydroxylic acid, is ubiquitous despite its dangers. Although the government promises to regulate DHMO and limit its destructive potential, it is often powerless to do so, and thousands of lives are lost every year.

DHMO can cause symptoms ranging from mild eye irritation to death. Prolonged exposure causes visible changes to the skin. At certain temperatures it causes severe and sometimes irreparable tissue damage, and inhaling it can cause respiratory and cardiac arrest. Excessive ingestion can cause brain swelling, leading to vomiting, confusion, seizures, coma and death.

DHMO is in your food and drink, in your medications and cosmetics, in the very air you breathe. You soak in it, your children play in it. In fact, DHMO is essential to your life and a lack of it is also fatal.

With the chemical formula H_2O, or two hydrogen atoms for every one of oxygen, we can call DHMO hydrogen hydroxide, oxidane or any number of other names, but mostly we just call it water. We can't live without it, but even clean, uncontaminated water can be toxic when misused.

The dose makes the poison

Every substance you encounter in your daily life, no matter how beneficial or necessary for health, can be poisonous if you ingest, inhale or absorb enough of it.

But the opposite is also true: Any substance can be non-toxic or minimally toxic. It all depends on the amount, duration and route of exposure.

Modern household products are generally designed to be very low toxicity, but they are poisons in the same way that everything on earth is a poison.

And also not a poison.

Why a Commonsense Guide?

Nothing in life is to be feared, it is only to be understood.
Now is the time to understand more, so that we may fear less.

- Marie Curie

Even though the products we buy have been largely formulated with safety in mind, we are constantly bombarded with warnings about **toxins** and **hidden dangers**.

These scary messages cause a low level of fear and anxiety that skyrockets when a product you rely on ends up in a mouth or eye where it doesn't belong.

My years at poison control convinced me a book was needed to help parents and others think rationally about common household products, and to confidently and effectively manage accidental exposures. This requires knowing what's in your products and how they work.

When the unexpected happens

When your child bites into a glow stick or you mistake super glue for eye drops, the first thing you want to know is what to do and how much to worry. For each product you'll find that information right at the top of the page.

Then you'll find more in-depth information and, often, ideas for homemade or less-toxic alternatives. You can make your own diaper ointment, sidewalk chalk or toothpaste, dry flowers with silica gel and make decorative air freshener with the water-absorbing beads found in disposable diapers.

Of course, almost every household product will have ingredients someone considers unsafe. The information provided here has been gleaned from decades of research and experience, and is meant to help you with the kind of real-life exposures that can happen in any home.

You won't find much about environmental toxicity, special sensitivities or possible long-term effects of chronic exposures, but you will find out what to do on Halloween when the cat whiskers your daughter super-glued to her cheeks won't come off.

You know: Commonsense, everyday stuff.

What about chemicals?

By convention sweet is sweet, bitter is bitter, hot is hot, cold is cold, color is color. But in reality there are atoms and the void.

- Democritus

The word **"chemical"** is sometimes used as an epithet, to describe something that is man-made, toxic and dangerous.

However, chemistry is the study of matter, and **every single thing that has mass is by definition a chemical**. Water (H2O) is a chemical. So is oxygen (O2). So is sea salt (sodium chloride, NaCl).

Kale's chemical components include 3-indoyl-methyl-glucosinolate, glucobrassicanapin and N-methyl-phenethylamine, among many others. The expression **"chemical free"** has no meaning at all.

About pronounceability

Rather than being a sign of danger, a chemical's complex name simply means it's been studied and we know a lot about it.

The International Union of Pure and Applied Chemistry (IUPAC) has standardized the nomenclature, or naming system, of chemicals to make the names universally understood.

Those long chemical names with lots of numbers, hyphens and prefixes follow specific rules and conventions that allow them to convey a great deal of information. Every atom of a molecule is accounted for, as is its location and relation to the other atoms.

For example, can you pronounce this: **(5R)-5-[(1S)-1,2-Dihydroxyethyl]-3,4-dihydroxy-2(5H)-furanone**?

In most cases it's easier to just call it **vitamin C**. But the IUPAC name tells us everything we need to know to visualize it like this:

Like this:

Or even like this:

You can watch a fun Crash Course video on chemical nomenclature at:

youtu.be/U7wavimfNFE

Stuff parents say . . .

I don't know how he got it open. It has a child-proof cap.

By law, prescription medications and many other potentially harmful products must be sold in packaging that is **child-resistant**. There is no such thing as child-proof!

Keep in mind that child-resistant packaging is supposed to be difficult for a child to open, but it is not allowed to impede access for older adults or people with disabilities.

The most you can hope for is that child-resistant packaging will slow your child down long enough for you to intervene, but even that isn't guaranteed. Once a child learns to open a child-resistant package, they are unlikely to ever forget.

I don't know how she got it. It was up really high.

Children are natural explorers, and some are more adventurous than others. For these children, the very fact you are trying to keep something away from them means it must be interesting, and putting it up high just challenges them to find a way to reach it. It's safer to keep medications in a toolbox or tackle box that can be padlocked; cleaning supplies and other large items can go in a locking file cabinet.

The label says it's non-toxic—is it?

Some products have to meet set requirements to be labeled non-toxic, others don't. Art supplies, for example, are well-regulated and if you see an AP label you know the product is non-toxic.

All products sold in the US have a general obligation to be safe, or to carry appropriate warnings if they are not.

Of course, that doesn't mean dangerous products are never sold; sometimes they are, and enforcement of safety standards is ongoing. But the emphasis is on identifying products that are harmful rather than the ones that are not. That leaves us with few standards for non-toxic labelling.

If a product is labeled "non-toxic" but lacks certification, it means according to the manufacturer it doesn't contain anything that is known to cause harm with reasonably proper use.

I looked it up on the internet, and now I'm totally freaked out.

Please, please, please call poison control first, before going to the internet. Believe it or not, you will read things there that are not true.

I feel like a terrible parent.

You *should* feel like a terrible parent if you intentionally give your child something you know is harmful, or if you know your child is in danger and do nothing. Otherwise, you should realize it's a child's job to explore her environment, forgive yourself for being human, and plan to do better in the future.

I haven't done anything yet. I didn't know what to do.

You can be ready for accidents if you plan ahead. Read up on managing ingestions, eye exposures and skin exposures now, so you'll know what to do when something happens. If all else fails, remember this number: 800-222-1222.

I made him puke.

Although that seemed like a good idea at the time, it wasn't. Now and then someone gets lucky and forced vomiting brings up the sought-after item, but whereas the item itself probably wasn't harmful to start with, that invasive maneuver was both traumatic and dangerous.

The American Academy of Pediatrics issued a policy statement almost 15 years ago against forced vomiting, recommending parents call poison control (800-222-1222) instead.

Should I make him puke? (Or: Should I get some ipecac?)

No.

I tried to rinse her eyes/mouth, but she wouldn't let me.

Parenting is hard work, and sometimes it isn't fun. If your child is in pain and you can't manage irrigation at home, you'll have to go to the emergency room.

So what should I watch for (after being told exposure is not toxic)?

You should watch for normal behavior and lack of symptoms. Call poison control or your health care provider if you see something else.

Do we need to go to the emergency room?

Here's the bottom line: You're the parent, and you have the right to seek medical care for your child whenever you feel it's needed, no matter what anyone else tells you. Whether you need to go is another matter.

In most cases if your child appears fine, the ER won't be needed. In these cases, the choice is yours. Sometimes, though, you must go in no matter what (eg, ingestion of button batteries, multiple magnets and some drugs). You can always rely on poison control or your health care provider to help figure this out.

I got scared because the label said to call poison control.

Poison control is always there to help, and you should always call with any poison-related questions or concerns. This helpful suggestion on the label doesn't mean the product is dangerous.

We're really careful at home, but the home we're visiting isn't child-proofed.

When you're visiting folks who don't have young children—even if they did once upon a time—you should assume the house isn't child-proofed and keep your little ones within sight. It wouldn't be impolite to ask if there are any medications or other potentially harmful things within reach, though, and to ask to have them put away while you're there.

I only turned my back for a minute.

That's all it takes.

I know he is telling me the truth, because he doesn't lie.

Children don't really understand the difference between truth and make-believe before they are 5 or 6 years old, so we consider young children "unreliable historians" rather than liars.

I know she is telling me the truth, because she is really, really smart.

Your child may be quite intelligent, but that doesn't mean she won't go through the same developmental stages as any other child.

He knows he isn't supposed to.

Before about the age of 6 children have very little ability to internalize rules. Your toddler or preschooler may behave well when you're paying attention, because your presence helps him remember what he is and isn't supposed to do.

But left unattended he is likely to go where his curiosity takes him, and your rules won't follow along. It's important to remember this is normal for his age and doesn't mean he's being disobedient.

You can't rely on your young child to police herself and it isn't fair to punish her when she eats those delicious vitamins that look and taste like candy, even though you told her not to. You just have to pay attention, keep reminding her of the rules and know that somewhere around first grade she'll develop the ability to remind herself.

Poisoning First Aid

Poisoning First Aid

Ingestions & Oral Exposures

What to do

1 Wipe or rinse the mouth First wipe any residue, such as ointment or pill fragments, from the mouth

Adults and children four years and older can swish plain water around in the mouth and spit it out. For younger children, rinse the mouth with a dripping wet washcloth.

What to expect

Most household products are harmless when **tasted**, although some may **irritate** the mouth.

When **swallowed**, some irritate the throat or stomach and may cause **gagging**, a **burning** sensation or **vomiting**. This may be brief but in some cases will require medical care.

2 Drink plain water or another mild liquid An adult should drink about **8 ounces**, and a child about **4 ounces**. You are trying to rinse the throat and dilute anything that made it to the stomach, not flush it out.

Drinking too much too quickly can cause nausea or other discomfort. If a child refuses an offer of fluids, a **popsicle** or **ice cream** may also work.

3 In some cases medical treatment may be needed, so check product listings here and call **poison control** at **(800) 222-1222** for personal advice that is specific to your situation.

Make this call **before going to the internet**, as what you read there may not apply to you.

Warning
Call **911** instead of the poison center for
loss of consciousness or trouble breathing or swallowing.

Home treatments that are not used

Ipecac

Parents were once advised to have ipecac on hand for poisoning emergencies. Derived from a plant in the same family as coffee, ipecac irritates the stomach and causes vomiting.

Ipecac is no longer used because vomiting is not an effective way to remove a potential poison from the stomach. In fact, ipecac causes vomiting that may be more dangerous than whatever was originally ingested and can interfere with effective treatment.

Ipecac can also be abused by those with eating disorders. Chronic ipecac abuse can cause serious—even fatal—damage to the heart. If you still have ipecac in your medicine cabinet, you should discard it now.

Forced vomiting

Never put your finger down a child's throat to make them vomit. It's not helpful or necessary and your child will truly be in danger if you injure the delicate tissue at the back of the throat. This kind of injury can cause the airway to bleed and swell, making it hard for the child to breathe.

Activated charcoal

Activated charcoal is regular charcoal that has been crushed into small particles and treated to make the particles porous, like tiny sponges, so they can **adsorb** toxins. This means some (but not all) substances will stick to the charcoal particles and be carried out of the body.

The activated charcoal used in emergency rooms is a very fine powder that is mixed with liquid to the consistency of a smoothie. Used this way, activated charcoal can prevent **some** potential poisons from being absorbed into the body. The amount of charcoal given, and the way it is given, depends on the patient and is not without risk; it is meant to be used under medical supervision.

Activated charcoal tablets

Activated charcoal tablets are sold over the counter and may be helpful for treating diet-related intestinal discomfort, but they are **not for emergency use** and should not be given as a home treatment for poisoning.

Foreign bodies

Objects that remain whole when swallowed and as they pass through the GI tract are called foreign bodies.

Most foreign bodies pass uneventfully (even sharp ones) but any abdominal pain or change in appetite or bowel movements after ingestion of a foreign body should be medically evaluated.

There are a few foreign bodies that require medical attention even if there are no symptoms, including disc batteries, magnets (if more than one is swallowed) and anything that contains lead.

Always check with poison control (800-222-1222) or your health care provider if you have any questions about these or any other foreign bodies.

Poisoning First Aid

Eye Exposures

What to do

1 Irrigate At home irrigation is done most effectively in the shower. Run any temperature water you find comfortable and stand facing the water, letting it hit your forehead and run over your face.

It isn't necessary to hold your eyes open, just keep blinking as the water runs over them.

If a shower is not available, use another source of clean, running water. For example, if you are outside and all you have nearby is a garden hose, use it. As long as the water is clean, don't delay irrigation while looking for a better source.

If the exposure is to one eye and you have to use a faucet, turn your head so the affected eye is lower than the unaffected eye. This will keep the contaminant from running into the unaffected eye.

2 If your child won't tolerate the shower Run a bath of plain water (no bubble bath) and make a game of it with lots of splashing and pouring. As with the shower, the child just needs to blink while the water runs over her face. It may be helpful to have another child in the tub.

3 How long to do it You usually want to irrigate for at least 15 minutes, although for caustic substances (like degreasers or toilet bowl cleaners) you may need to continue for 30 minutes. Setting a timer or having someone else watch the time for you will help make sure you irrigate long enough.

4 If you are wearing contact lenses remove them before or during irrigation and discard them.

After irrigating

Tap water can be hard on the eyes and after irrigation they will likely feel a little dry and irritated. Let them rest for another 15 minutes to return to normal. You may find it helpful to lay down, close your eyes and lay a cool washcloth over them.

Don't use medicated drops after an eye exposure. They can irritate your eyes even more and make it hard to determine whether you need medical care.

What's normal

Your eyes may be pink and a little puffy after irrigating them, and your vision may be slightly hazy for a short time.

What's not normal

Pain, any vision change that doesn't clear up quickly, or feeling like there is sand or an eyelash in your eye. These suggest injury to the cornea and require immediate medical attention. Failing to get treatment for an eye injury may lead to permanent vision loss.

Don't ask a small child if her eyes hurt. Let her return to normal activities and watch for signs of irritation such as excessive blinking, watering or rubbing. If irrigation doesn't clear these up, or if you are not able to perform a thorough irrigation, your child will need medical attention.

Getting medical care

If medical care is needed, it is usually best to go to an emergency room. A thorough eye exam requires a slit lamp, which is a kind of upright microscope used to look closely for injuries. Emergency rooms always have slit lamps but most doctor's offices and urgent care clinics don't.

For a minor corneal abrasion you will likely be sent home with an antibiotic ointment, a pain reliever and instructions to follow up with an opthamologist. If you have a severe injury, they will try to bring in a specialist to see you right away.

Poisoning First Aid

Skin Exposures

What to do

1 **Washing with soap and water** is the most important treatment for every skin exposure.

For irritating or corrosive substances the initial gentle washing should be followed by irrigation with copious amounts of running water.

Soaking the affected area in still water may prolong the exposure rather than removing the substance from the skin.

2 **Don't try to neutralize** an acid by adding baking soda, or an alkali by adding vinegar.

Neutralization is a powerful chemical reaction that breaks molecular bonds and releases energy in the form of heat; this can be more damaging than the original exposure.

The proper treatment for these exposures is irrigation with copious amounts of water. Begin irrigation immediately and call poison control for advice on what to do next.

3 **How long to do it** Most skin exposures only need a simple wash and rinse, but some (eg, drain openers) may need longer irrigation and some (eg, super glue, jalapeno peppers) may need more than just washing.

Check the page for each product to find out if this applies, or call poison control for specific recommendations.

What to expect

This is highly variable and depends on the product, but most household products have mild effects, if any.

Getting medical care

Generally speaking, medical care is needed for skin exposures that result in injury or pain, especially if the face, hands or genitals are involved.

There are a few products that have special risks or need specific treatment, but always begin irrigation before looking the product up in this book or calling poison control for further advice.

Inhalation Exposures

What to do

1 **Fresh air** Move away from the inhalant. If the exposure occurs inside, go outside. Do not go back in if you are coughing or having trouble breathing. If it is safe to enter or remain, open all door and windows. Placing a fan in an open window or door, turned so it is blowing outward, will pull fumes out of the room.

2 **Breathing steam** is not a substitute for medical care but can be very soothing for mild airway irritation. Stand in or next to a hot shower, or pour boiling water into a bowl and breathe in the steam.

3 **Medical care** is needed for respiratory symptoms that don't resolve with first aid measures, or if rescue meds or other usual measures don't ease symptoms of asthma or COPD that have been triggered by the exposure.

Aspiration

Aspiration occurs when something that is swallowed "goes down the wrong pipe," entering the airway Instead the stomach. This is usually followed by a spasm of involuntary, reflexive **coughing**.

Any kind of aspiration can cause significant illness, but aspiration of a **hydrocarbon** such as **gasoline** (p. 98) or **mineral oil** (p. 38) is especially dangerous.

Suspected aspiration **requires medical evaluation** even if the person seems fine after the coughing stops, as more severe symptoms may develop hours later.

Inhalant abuse

Many common household products can be abused. In addition to short-term effects like slurred speech and impaired judgment, chronic abuse of inhalants can lead to violent behavior, hearing loss, brain damage and death.

Many of those who succumb to what is known as **sudden sniffing death syndrome** (SSDS) are abusing inhalants for the very first time.

Inhalant abuse—or suspected abuse—is life-threatening, and intervention is urgently needed.

POISON CONTROL 800-222-1222

Product Listings

Toxicity terms

Anything can be toxic or not, depending on the route, length and amount of exposure. Individual differences matter, too; something that causes no problems for one person may be quite dangerous for another.

These terms are used in this book as general guidelines, not as a guarantee of safety or toxicity.

» **Not toxic** No symptoms are expected from any kind of exposure.

» **Minimally toxic** May cause minor symptoms that can be managed at home.

» **Toxic** At least some exposures may cause significant symptoms, and medical care may be needed.

» **Highly toxic** While some very limited exposures may be managed at home, many exposures will require medical care.

» **Extremely toxic** Significant exposures may cause life-altering injury or death.

Acne treatments

How toxic: Not toxic to minimally toxic

Mouth	**Skin**	**Eyes**	**Inhalation**
May dry or irritate ▼ Rinse mouth	*May be irritating with regular use* ▼ Wash affected area	*May be irritating* ▼ Irrigate	*Not expected*

What to expect

All acne treatments can be irritating to skin even when used as directed, and they may irritate eyes and mouth.

In products designed for use on skin the concentration of active ingredients are too small to be toxic when ingested.

Common ingredients

Topical acne treatments are designed to control bacteria, clear clogged follicles and encourage growth of healthy skin cells.

Benzoyl peroxide kills *P. acnes,* a bacterium that feeds on skin oils and causes inflammation in pores. Its drying effects may help clear oil and dead skin cells from pores as well. Over-the-counter products contain from 2.5% to 10% benzoyl peroxide; higher concentrations are no more more effective against acne but are more likely to irritate skin. Benzoyl peroxide also has bleaching properties and can discolor fabrics.

Retinoids encourage shedding of dead skin cells and growth of healthy new cells, helping to keep pores unclogged. They are chemically related to vitamin A and are also used in anti-aging products. Opinions differ as to whether retinoids increase risk of sunburn, but the products can be inactivated by sun exposure. Some retinoids should not be used with benzoyl peroxide as it can counteract them.

Salicylic acid, a chemical cousin of aspirin, helps clear out pore-clogging dead skin cells and also reduces inflammation. It may be listed as **beta hydroxy acid** on some labels.

Alpha hydroxy acids include glycolic, lactic and citric acids, which were originally derived from sugar, milk and fruit, respectively; they can all be produced synthetically as well. They are effective exfoliants that slough off dead skin cells from the surface of skin and stimulate the growth of new cells. They are used in high concentrations in chemical peels.

Sulfur may be the least effective treatment on the list but it is considered the kindest to skin and the least likely to cause irritation. It clears away excess oil, exfoliates dead skin cells and has antibacterial properties. It is usually found in combination with other acne products.

About acne

There are different kinds of acne, but most over-the-counter products are intended for the kind that strikes in adolescence. Hormonal changes cause the sebaceous glands to secrete excessive amounts of oily **sebum** into hair follicles.

Sebum can become trapped in pores, mixing with dead skin cells and providing a feeding ground for bacteria known as **Propionibacterium acnes** (*P. acnes*). *P. acnes* is always present on the skin but grows more rapidly as puberty approaches.

It is believed the redness, swelling and pus associated with acne is caused by infection with *P. acnes*, but recent studies suggest at least some acne is caused by inflammation unrelated to *P. acnes*. The treatment of acne is likely to evolve over time as we learn more about its causes.

Diet & acne

Current research suggests that **high-glycemic-index foods** that cause a rapid increase in blood sugar may contribute to acne. It is believed the frequent bursts of insulin needed to counter spikes in blood sugar cause inflammation and hormonal changes that make acne worse. Limiting high-glycemic-index foods in the diet is thought to have a number of other health benefits as well.

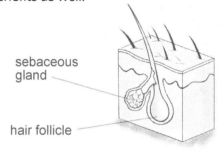

sebaceous gland

hair follicle

 ## Make your own topical acne treatment

Tea tree oil

Tea tree oil (p. 168) has antimicrobial and anti-inflammatory properties and is as effective as benzoyl peroxide in treating acne. It may take longer to work but it is also less irritating.

Pure tea tree oil is very strong and should be diluted before use. Add a few drops to water and swab on with a cotton ball, or add to a clay mask, moisturizer or unmedicated face wash.

Green tea

Green tea has anti-inflammatory and anti-oxidant properties and may be helpful both taken by mouth and applied directly to the skin. The active components of green tea degrade quickly and it should be used as soon as possible after brewing.

Aspirin

Aspirin can be crushed, mixed with water and applied directly to a problem spot. Use of aspirin by any route is not recommended for children or teens with recent viral illness.

A&D ointment

How toxic: Not toxic

Mouth	Skin	Eyes	Inhalation
Not toxic	*Not toxic*	*May be irritating*	*Not expected*
▼	▼	▼	
Rinse mouth	Wash affected area	Irrigate	

What to expect

A&D ointments contain very small amounts of vitamins and are not toxic when ingested, but a child could gag and vomit if they object to the oily texture.

Large ingestions, which are unlikely, may have a mild laxative effect because the ointment has an oily base.

Common ingredients

The benefits of A&D ointments are due to their base oils rather than vitamin content, which is minimal.

Vitamins A and D in the diet are essential to good health. Because they are fat soluble they can accumulate in body tissues, but it isn't possible to get enough of either vitamin from A&D ointment to be toxic.

Petrolatum is another name for petroleum jelly (p. 152) and is the active ingredient in most A&D ointments. The petrolatum forms a barrier that protects skin from irritants so it can heal.

Mineral oil is a petroleum distillate traditionally used in baby oil (p. 38). Food grade mineral oil is sometimes taken by mouth as an emollient laxative, which lubricates the GI tract so stool moves more smoothly.

Light mineral oil is a less dense form of mineral oil that is otherwise the same as far as use and toxicity.

Lanolin (p. 124) is a wax secreted by the sebaceous glands of sheep to help condition and protect their skin and wool. Lanolin doesn't form an effective barrier like petrolatum, but it's closer in composition to our natural oils and does a better job of softening and moisturizing.

Cod liver oil is taken from the livers of cod, fish of the genus *Gadus* found in the Atlantic and Pacific oceans. Cod feed near the ocean floor and while their livers are oily their flesh is not; fish oil supplements are made from other kinds of fish.

Cod liver oil for consumption is obtained by steaming or crushing the livers, breaking open cell walls so the oil is released. Oil from livers that were simply allowed to rot was once used commercially for lamp oil, paint and other applications.

Cod liver oil is added to ointments because it contains vitamins A and D, but you will find it listed on the label as an inactive ingredient because the amount of those vitamins is so low as to be literally immeasurable.

Microcrystalline waxes are petroleum derivatives that are used to bind the other ingredients. Their tiny crystals form a flexible lattice that holds oil tightly within it, keeping ointment ingredients from separating. The waxes also give the ointment a firmer consistency and help it stick to skin. Food grade microcrystalline waxes are used in numerous foods, cosmetics and pharmaceuticals.

Light liquid paraffin is another kind of mineral oil that creates a barrier to protect skin. It's also used as a lubricant in ointments for dry eyes.

Getting A&D out of hair

Pat in cornstarch until the ointment is well-absorbed, then wash with a clarifying shampoo or degreasing hand dishwashing liquid (Dawn® is the standard).

It may take repeated shampooing to get A&D ointment out of a child's hair. Sleeping on a towel between washings helps absorb the oil and protect bedding.

Getting A&D out of fabric

Gently scrape off as much ointment as possible with a spoon or dull knife. Dab the stain with a cotton ball soaked in rubbing alcohol (p. 156), then blot with paper towels. Repeat as necessary. When you can't see any more ointment on the fabric, wash the spot with degreasing hand dishwashing liquid (Dawn® again) and rinse well. Launder as usual.

Make your own vitamin ointment or cream

Petroleum jelly (p. 152) is the primary ingredient of most A&D ointments, and while it contains no vitamins, you can apply it directly to skin to form a protective barrier. The same is true of mineral oil and lanolin.

Vitamins A and D are beneficial to skin, but the amounts found in A&D ointments is probably too low to provide any real benefit. You can add vitamins to your homemade ointments and creams, but keep in mind that vitamins in liquid form are going to include other ingredients—like glycerin, natural and synthetic oils and fats, preservatives and flavoring agents—that you may be trying to avoid.

Cod liver oil capsules and most liquid oils will have other ingredients added, but it is possible to find it in a form that is virtually pure. Cod liver oil will turn rancid over time; if you add it to a homemade mixture the resulting product should be stored according to the instructions on the cod liver oil label.

Shea butter contains vitamins A and E. It is sold in both raw and refined forms; the raw form will have a higher nutritional content. Recipes for shea butter creams abound, most starting with equal parts shea butter and coconut oil.

Air fresheners

How toxic: Not toxic to minimally toxic, but toxic when abused

Mouth	**Skin**	**Eyes**	**Inhalation**
May be irritating	*Not toxic*	*May be irritating*	*Toxic when abused*
▼	▼	▼	▼
Rinse mouth	Wash affected area	Irrigate	See page 19

What to expect

A child may be attracted to an air freshener, especially if it smells like food, but it only takes a taste to realize their mistake.

Mild oral irritation is possible but confusion over why it smells so good and tastes so bad is more likely.

Common ingredients

The products most likely to be involved in accidental exposures are liquids for plug-in devices and diffuser reeds, especially when they smell like cinnamon, vanilla or other dessert ingredients.

Fragrances are the primary ingredients of air fresheners. Some are derived directly from natural sources, but the only way to be sure a product smells exactly the way you expect every time you use it is to synthesize fragrances in a lab. Natural materials such as flowers and leaves are analyzed for their molecular composition, then the needed molecules are built and mixed to recreate the original scent.

Essential oils could be toxic in large ingestions, but they don't taste as good as they smell and more than a taste is highly unlikely. Aspiration, while unlikely to occur, would require medical evaluation (see page 19 for more information on aspiration).

Neutralizers either bind with odor molecules or alter them in some other way so they don't fit into olfactory receptors.

Cyclodextrins are donut-shaped starch molecules that trap other molecules in their holes. They are used as carriers in medications, cosmetics and foods, but in air fresheners they capture odor molecules.

Sanitizers kill bacteria, both for hygienic reasons and because bacteria are tiny odor factories; they take in molecules that don't stink and repackage them into molecules that do. Common sanitizers are alcohols like **triethylene glycol** and cationic surfactants like **benzalkonium chloride**.

Propellants are gases kept under pressure in aerosol cans that launch fragrances, deodorizers and sanitizers into the air when the button is pressed. Propellants are usually petroleum products like propane and butane and are very dangerous when intentionally inhaled.

Air fresheners and the brain

We are able to smell things when they **volatilize**, or give off molecules that float in the air. We breathe in those molecules and they bind to olfactory receptors in the nasal cavity that connect directly to the brain. (Read more on page 151.)

Signals from odor receptors are distributed rapidly to different parts of the brain, provoking memories and emotions even before conscious thought.

What's the difference?

Air fresheners are designed to emit molecules that we find pleasurable, like ripe fruit, warm cookies and sweet flowers.

Neutralizers capture or deactivate molecules we would rather not detect, like stale cigarette smoke and rotting food.

Sanitizers kill bacteria that through normal metabolism release molecules we find unpleasant, like thiols metabolized from sweat.

 ## Make your own air freshener

Deodorizing spray

1 ounce unflavored vodka or gin
6 ounces distilled water
Essential oil(s)

» Mix in spray bottle and use as needed.

Coffee

Freshly ground beans or used grounds

» Place in an open dish, jar or can to adsorb odors in refrigerator, microwave or room. Pack into a sock or other fabric pouch to absorb odors in cooler or lunch box.

Reed diffuser

Neutral oil to fill container (safflower and sweet almond oil are often recommended)
    OR distilled water to fill container
Dash of rubbing alcohol or plain vodka
Essential oil(s)
Reeds purchased from craft store, or bamboo skewers

» Mix oil or water, alcohol and essential oils and pour into a ceramic container with a small neck. Insert diffuser reeds or bamboo skewers that are twice as long as the container is tall. Reed diffusers are more porous and will work better with oil-based mixtures. Flip the reeds or skewers every few days or as the exposed portion dries out.

Ammonia
How toxic: Minimally toxic to toxic

Mouth	**Skin**	**Eyes**	**Inhalation**
May be irritating	*May be irritating*	*Likely to be irritating*	*Fumes may be irritating*
▼	▼	▼	▼
Rinse mouth	Wash affected area	Copious irrigation for 30 minutes	Fresh air

What to expect

Household ammonia is very dilute and rarely causes serious injury, but its fumes can be very irritating to eyes, nose and throat. When ingested it can burn mucous membranes, but its strong smell and taste make anything more than a sip unlikely.

Ammonia splashed in the eyes can cause serious injury and medical evaluation after irrigation is almost always advised.
Any exposure to highly concentrated (28%–30%) ammonia is likely to require medical attention.

Warning
Never mix **ammonia** with **bleach**, as the resulting **chloramine gas** is a strong respiratory irritant. See page 43 for more information.

Common ingredients
The product label may say it contains ammonium hydroxide, which just means ammonia in water.

Ammonia is useful as a household cleaner because it is alkaline enough to turn fats and oils into soap, a process known as **saponification** (see page 162). Household ammonia is between 90% and 98% water, which helps to rinse away saponified soil.

Unfortunately the fats under our skin can also be saponified by strongly alkaline substances. Household ammonia isn't expected to cause this kind of injury, but it can still be destructive to eyes and to delicate mucous membranes in the mouth and throat.

Surfactants may be added to increase cleaning power.

Fragrance is sometimes added to make ammonia's pungent odor less noticeable.

Highly concentrated (28%–30%) ammonia is a specialty product that has scientific, industrial and craft applications and has to be handled with great care, using personal protection gear like heavy gloves, face masks and respirators.
This kind of ammonia has no place in a household setting.

Other uses & kinds of ammonia

Baker's ammonia (ammonium carbonate) was used as a leavening agent hundreds of years before baking soda and baking powder came on the market. It was once derived from deer antlers and known as **hartshorn**, but now it's made by combining ammonia and carbon dioxide.

Like other leavening agents, baker's ammonia vaporizes during baking, creating tiny air pockets to expand the dough. It's only used in cookies and crackers like **Speculoos** that are thin enough for all the ammonia gas to escape and that benefit from an extra-crispy texture. Baker's ammonia can be substituted 1:1 for baking soda or powder in any cookie recipe, but using baking soda or powder in a recipe calling for baker's ammonia will result in a heavier, less crisp cookie.

Smelling salts (ammonium carbonate) have such a noxious odor and irritating effect that inhaling them results in a sharp intake of breath, increasing alertness. Once popular as a **lady reviver** for Victorian women prone to fainting spells, smelling salts are still available in capsule form for first aid kits. They are also used as a performance enhancer by weight lifters and other athletes. Smelling salts should never be used on someone with a head injury, as the temporary boost in alertness may cover up a medical emergency.

Salmiak is black licorice made with **ammonium chloride**, which combines the salty chloride flavor with the kick of ammonia. It's popular in northern Germany and Scandinavia. There are other varieties of candy made with ammonium chloride, as well as salmiak-flavored vodkas.

Ammonia fuming is the process of placing wood in an enclosed space with highly concentrated liquid ammonia. The ammonia reacts with tannins in the wood, causing it to darken. The longer the exposure, the darker the wood. Fuming enhances wood grain without obscuring it and the darkened effect is permanent. After fuming the wood can be varnished or oiled.

Ammonia fuming was popular during the Arts and Crafts movement of the late 19th and early 20th centuries. Because fuming essentially speeds up a process that would occur naturally over a much longer period of time, it's considered by some to be a more authentic, natural way to color wood than staining or painting.

Ammonia in the body

Ammonia is composed of nitrogen and hydrogen. Nitrogen is needed to build amino acids, protein, DNA and chlorophyll, and so is critical to every form of life.

Almost 80% of the air we breathe is nitrogen, but we can't use it in that form. Bacteria in soil convert nitrogen absorbed from the air (and from fertilizers, page 84) to a form that can be taken up by plants, which we can then eat.

Every cell in our body needs nitrogen to function, but it eventually becomes a waste product and is excreted from cells in the form of ammonia. Ammonia is then converted in the liver to urea and is excreted in urine (p. 176).

Excessive ammonia is neurotoxic, and diseases of the liver or kidneys can cause ammonia to build up in the brain with severe consequences.

Ant & roach traps

How toxic: Not toxic

Mouth	**Skin**	**Eyes**	**Inhalation**
Not toxic	*Not toxic*	*Not expected*	*Not expected*
▼	▼		
Rinse mouth	Wash affected area		

What to expect

A dog might be able to chew through a trap's plastic housing but a child cannot. Sucking on packaging containing solid or paste bait won't get any of it out.

Even if accessed, the insecticides used in traps are too low in toxicity to cause more than perhaps mild irritation.

Common ingredients

Because ant and roach traps are often used around food, they are made with ingredients that are toxic to insects but not to mammals.

Borax (p. 46) is a mineral form of boron mined from dried lake beds. How it works on ants and roaches isn't entirely clear, but it's believed to sabotage their digestive systems. Borax kills slowly, allowing the bugs to carry it back to their nests.

Indoxacarb is metabolized by insects into a sodium channel blocker that interferes with transmission of nerve impulses and causes paralysis. Mammals don't metabolize indoxacarb in this way, making its toxicity very specific to insects.

Spinosad is derived from the soil bacterium *Saccharopolyspora spinosa*. It causes paralysis by stimulating the insect's nervous system to the point of exhaustion. Spinosad is safe for mammals to ingest and is used in oral flea control tablets for cats and dogs (p. 90).

Abamectin is a combination of two closely related forms of **avermectin**, a natural fermentation product of the soil-dwelling bacterium *Streptomyces avermitilis*. It's been used for years as a treatment for internal parasites and as a crop pesticide. It kills by interfering with the transmission of nerve impulses and causing paralysis. Mammals are not immune to abamectin but it would take a huge amount to be toxic.

Hydramethylnon works by disrupting cellular respiration, the process that converts food into fuel to meet the body's energy needs. The insect's bodily functions slowly run down until it dies. Extremely high doses would have to be ingested to cause illness in pets or people because mammals excrete hydramethylnon very quickly.

Fipronil blocks receptors for GABA, a neurotransmitter that prevents excessive nervous system activity. When GABA is unable to bind to its receptors the nervous system goes into overdrive, causing seizures, paralysis and death. Fipronil doesn't block GABA very effectively in mammals and is used in popular spot-on flea treatments for dogs and cats (p. 90).

Pheromones are odorant chemicals taken from roach droppings and are used to attract roaches to the bait station. Roach traps of the kind where roaches enter and get stuck inside, unable to leave, use pheromones to lure the roaches and contain no pesticides at all.

More about roaches

Cockroaches can live for several weeks without food but only about a week without water. In fact, because roaches **breathe through openings on their bodies** but drink through their mouths, they can live without a head right up until they die of dehydration.

More about ants

An ant's **petiole** is too narrow for solid food to pass, so they can only take in liquids; this is why many ant baits are in liquid form. Bait in solid or paste form is taken back to the nest where it is liquified by larvae and then ingested by the adult ants.

petiole

✍ Do your own ant & roach control

Diatomaceous earth (DE)

Ants and roaches are covered with a layer of waxy hydrocarbons that makes them water-tight. Diatomaceous earth (DE) is believed to disrupt this waxy coating and cause dehydration. It may also kill roaches when ingested.

  » Lay down a line of DE along baseboards and ant entryways to form a barrier ants may be reluctant to cross.

  » Mix DE with peanut butter to encourage roaches to eat it.

  » Use only food grade DE as products that are not food grade may contain heavy metals or other contaminants.

Like any fine particulate matter DE is a respiratory irritant when inhaled, so be careful when handling it. DE only works when dry; if it gets wet wipe it up and replace it.

Borax See page 47 for information on using borax as a pesticide.

Antibiotic ointment

How toxic: Not toxic but allergic reactions may occur

Mouth	**Skin**	**Eyes**	**Inhalation**
Not toxic	*Allergic reactions may occur*	*May be irritating*	*Not expected*
▼	▼	▼	
Rinse mouth	Discontinue use	Irrigate	

What to expect

The antibiotics in these products are not toxic when ingested, but large ingestions of oil-based products may cause mild diarrhea.

Persistent or increased symptoms after applying a product may indicate an allergic reaction; consult your health care provider.

Common ingredients

The antibiotics in OTC ointments and creams aren't toxic,
but allergic contact dermatitis, a type of skin sensitivity, is common.

Triple antibiotics contain **bacitracin**, **neomycin** and **polymyxins**, usually in a petroleum jelly base. They are used together to produce broad spectrum products that are effective against many kinds of bacteria. Skin sensitivities to individual antibiotics do occur and so products are also available that contain just one or two of them. All of these antibiotics are harvested from bacteria that produce them in order to kill other bacteria.

Bacitracin is produced by a bacterium called *Bacillus subtilis*. It was discovered in 1943 when it was found to inhibit Gram-positive bacteria in a patient's infected wound. (The name is a mashup of *Bacillus* and Tracy, the patient's last name.) Bacitracin is still produced by growing *B. subtilis* and is valued for its effectiveness against staph and strep bacteria. It's not taken orally due to risk of kidney damage.

Bacitracin doesn't affect the kidneys when applied to the skin, but some people may be allergic to it.

Neomycin is produced by the bacterium *Streptomyces fradiae* and is most effective against Gram-negative bacteria, although it is effective against some Gram-positive bacteria as well. It may exacerbate tinnitus and some kinds of hearing loss when taken orally, but does not have this kind of effect when applied to the skin. Sensitivity to neomycin is not uncommon and topical antibiotics without it are available.

Polymyxins, a group of antibiotics produced by the bacterium *Paenibacillus polymyxa*, are effective against Gram-negative bacteria. Although safe when applied to the skin, they are nephrotoxic and neurotoxic when given intravenously. They are not absorbed through the GI tract and so cannot be taken orally, and are used intravenously only as a last resort.

Pramoxine is a local anesthetic that interrupts the transmission of information between nerve cells. leading to numbness that relieves pain and itching. It's suitable for small wounds but not for large areas of broken skin. Allergic reactions to pramoxine are not common but do occur.

Medicinal honey

Antimicrobial ingredients in honey include **hydrogen peroxide**, a byproduct of glucose metabolism called **methylglyoxal**, and at least one peptide known as a **defensin**. Commercial products are formulated to ensure specific amounts of each.

Medihoney® is made from **Manuka** honey from New Zealand and Australia, which has more methylglyoxal. It takes longer to kill most pathogens but has a longer lasting effect.

Revamil® is produced in greenhouses in the Netherlands and has more hydrogen peroxide and bee defensin-1. It kills several pathogens quickly but becomes less effective with time and dilution.

If you are tempted to try the honey in your kitchen cupboard on a wound, there are a couple of caveats. One is that your culinary honey isn't sterile and may contain dangerous pathogens. Another is that many grocery store products contain honey imported from unknown sources (mainly in China) and have been ultra-filtered in an attempt to remove contaminants. This filtering may not remove all contaminants, and it may reduce the honey's natural healing properties.

Gram staining

Bacteria are **transparent** in their natural state. Before the bacteria in a biological sample can be identified they must be made visible by staining. This is done by using **gentian violet** (p. 100), also known as crystal violet, in a procedure named for Danish bacteriologist Hans Christian Gram, who developed it in 1884.

In Gram staining, bacteria are flooded with violet dye and washed. Bacteria that retain the dye are **Gram-positive** and those that don't are **Gram-negative**. The difference between them has to do with the structure and chemistry of their **cell walls**.

All bacteria have an enclosing **cell membrane**. For a few, such as the *Mycoplasma* species that live as parasites inside other cells, the membrane is sufficient. Most bacteria, though, are further surrounded by a cell wall that gives them shape, protects them from their environment and performs critical metabolic functions.

Gram-positive bacteria have thick but relatively simple cell walls that trap the violet dye. Gram-negative bacteria have more complex cell walls that release the violet dye when they are washed. To be effective, an antibiotic must be matched with a cell wall it can disrupt or pass through, so Gram-staining is an essential first step in treating a bacterial infection.

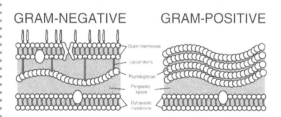

GRAM-NEGATIVE   GRAM-POSITIVE

Antifreeze

How toxic: Toxic to extremely toxic

Mouth	**Skin**	**Eyes**	**Inhalation**
Highly toxic	*May be irritating*	*May be irritating*	*Fumes may be irritating*
▼	▼	▼	▼
Rinse mouth	Wash affected area	Irrigate	Fresh air

What to expect

Ethylene glycol (EG) is sweet and nausea is not expected with just a taste. Ingestion of a full swallow or more of EG may cause intoxication similar to ethanol.

Medical care may not be needed for just a lick or taste; poison control can help you with this. Skin exposures and inhalation of fumes are not toxic but may be irritating.

> ### Warning
> Ingestion of ethylene glycol (green) antifreeze is an emergency and requires immediate medical attention.

Common ingredients

Antifreeze made with ethylene glycol is dyed fluorescent green.
The kind made with much less toxic propylene glycol is dyed pink.

Antifreeze keeps the water in a car's cooling system from freezing because it has a much lower freezing point than plain water. It also prevents overheating because it has a much higher boiling point than plain water. (See next page for more on this.)

Ethylene glycol (EG) is made from ethylene gas, which is produced by **cracking,** or breaking down, larger petroleum-based hydrocarbon molecules. (Ethylene gas is also produced by ripening fruit; this is how apples make bananas ripen faster.) New technologies are being developed to synthesize ethylene from renewable sources such as ethanol and methane.

Propylene glycol (PG) is a hydrocarbon derived from propene gas, which is also produced industrially by cracking larger petroleum-based hydrocarbon molecules. Propene is also given off during fermentation of glucose.

Unlike EG (see "Ethylene glycol poisoning," next page) PG's breakdown products, or metabolites—pyruvic acid, lactic acid, acetic acid—are components of normal biological processes and are not toxic.

PG has a number of useful characteristics and is widely used in foods, cosmetics and medications. Although it is non-toxic, there have been reported cases of allergic contact dermatitis due to such products.

Ethylene glycol poisoning

EG is an **alcohol**. When ingested it causes symptoms similar to ethanol intoxication. The real danger, though, is EG's toxic metabolites. **Glycolic acid**, for example, causes acidosis and interferes with critical metabolic processes. Glycolic acid breaks down into **oxalic acid**, which bonds with calcium to form **calcium oxalate**, the same compound kidney stones are made of. Calcium oxalate crystals can accumulate in the heart, central nervous system and kidneys, causing heart failure, meningitis, and renal failure. Untreated EG poisoning can be fatal.

How EG poisoning is treated

The primary goal in treating EG poisoning is to keep it from being broken down into its toxic metabolites. The enzyme that metabolizes EG would rather bind with ethanol, and ethanol can be given by mouth or IV as a treatment. An antidote called **fomepizole** that blocks the enzyme without the intoxicating effects of ethanol is preferred. If the EG is already being metabolized treatment may include IV sodium bicarbonate and/or hemodialysis.

Understanding boiling & freezing points

When we think **boiling** we think **hot**, and when we think **freezing** we think **cold**, because water boils at 212 degrees F, which compared to our body temperature is very hot, and it freezes at 32 F, which to us is very cold.

However, in scientific terms boiling and freezing points have to do with **energy levels**, not temperature.

A **liquid**'s molecules move around each other at a moderate speed and stay relatively close. The liquid **boils** when its molecules gain enough energy to fly apart from one another and launch themselves into the air, turning to vapor. It **freezes** when its molecules are so drained of energy that they stop moving past each other and stay fixed in place.

Water molecules are moderately bound to one another, and the amount of energy needed to make them fly apart and turn to vapor feels extremely hot to us. On the other hand propane, as an example, has molecules that are much more weakly bound and will vaporize at -43.6 F, giving it a boiling point that is far colder than what we think of as freezing.

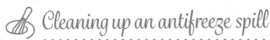 *Cleaning up an antifreeze spill*

Antifreeze may be rinsed onto the lawn but not into a storm or household drain.

» Remove children and pets from the area.

» Pour cat litter, sand or baking soda on the spill, then cover with paper towels. Leave in place for one hour.

» Use dry paper towels to wipe up the absorbent materials and bag them.

» Add liquid dish or laundry detergent to any remaining antifreeze and scrub with a stiff brush. Rinse or wipe with wet sponge, rag or paper towels; bag and dispose.

Automatic dishwasher detergent

How toxic: Minimally toxic

Mouth	**Skin**	**Eyes**	**Inhalation**
May be irritating	*Not toxic*	*May be irritating*	*Not expected*
▼	▼	▼	
Rinse mouth	Wash affected area	Irrigate	

What to expect

Dishwasher detergents can be more irritating than hand dishwashing soaps, but harmful ingestions are very rare. A typical exposure occurs when a toddler sticks a finger in dispenser residue and take a taste. Single-dose dishwasher packets have not been found to be more toxic than other automatic dishwasher detergents.

Common ingredients

Automatic dishwasher detergents (ADD) are more complex than hand dishwashing liquids and contain solvents, water softeners, anti-redeposition and anti-sudsing agents, and other ingredients specific to machine washing.

Sodium carbonate is also known as soda ash or washing soda (see page 178 for detailed information). In ADD it helps dissolve oils and greasy food residue and softens water. It's also used as a pH adjuster and is a common food additive.

Sodium percarbonate is sodium carbonate compounded with hydrogen peroxide, which forms an oxidizer that bleaches stains on dishes.

Alcohol alkoxylates are nonionic (having a neutral charge) surfactants that don't foam up when agitated.

Dipropylene glycol is a solvent and lubricant that helps remove grease and oil from dishes and prevents them from re-depositing.

Sodium silicate softens water by binding minerals like calcium and magnesium, keeping them from interfering with detergents and building up on metal parts in the dishwasher.

Complex phosphates keep minerals in the water (mostly calcium and magnesium) in solution so they don't bind with food and stick to dishes.

Hydrozincite protects glassware from other compounds in ADD, some of which can corrode the glass surface or leach metal ions from the glass. See page 70 for more information on zinc.

Boric acid serves a function very much like complex phosphates. See borax, page 46, for related information.

Rinse aids

Rinse aids are added to the dishwasher's rinse cycle, but their purpose is to help dishes dry faster. When water droplets sit on your clean dishes too long their slow evaporation can leave mineral residue behind, especially on glasses and glass dishes.

Rinse aids use **nonionic surfactants** to ease water's surface tension so it flows off glasses and dishes instead of beading up. **Citric acid** binds minerals so they rinse off instead of sticking.

It is possible to use **vinegar** instead of a commercial rinse aid, but doing so may damage synthetic rubber seals inside the dishwasher. The vinegar can either be placed in the rinse aid compartment before starting the washer or placed in a bowl or cup on the top rack during the rinse cycle.

Can you use hand dishwashing liquid in a dishwasher?

In a word, no.

Conditions inside your automatic dishwasher are very different from those in your kitchen sink.

The mounds of sudsy bubbles hand dishwashing liquids produce would at best make machine washing less effective, and at worst spill out of the dishwasher onto the kitchen floor.

It's the same reason you can't use dishwashing liquid in your clothes washer—all that agitation and fast-moving water whips up a voluminous froth, much like whipping egg whites into meringue.

 *Make your own automatic dishwasher detergent*

1 cup borax
1 cup washing soda
½ cup citric acid
   OR 3 teaspoons unsweetened lemonade mix
½ cup kosher salt
Optional: Unopened silica gel (p. 158) packets

» Mix all ingredients and store in an air-tight container.

» Adding unopened silica gel packets will help prevent clumping.

» Use 1 heaping tablespoon per wash.

» If spotting occurs, vinegar or another rinse aid may be added. Check dishwasher manufacturer instructions first as use of vinegar may not be advised.

Baby oil

How toxic: Not toxic unless aspirated

Mouth	Skin	Eyes	Inhalation
Not toxic	*Not toxic*	*May be irritating*	*Not expected but see aspiration warning below*
▼	▼	▼	
Rinse mouth	Wash affected area	Irrigate	

What to expect

Baby oil is not toxic when ingested but may cause mild vomiting due to its texture. A full swallow may have a mild laxative effect.

Aspiration

Coughing or changes in breathing after baby oil ingestion require immediate medical attention to rule out aspiration (see below).

Warning

Aspiration occurs when a swallowed substance goes down the **airway** rather than into the stomach. This is uncommon but serious. Aspiration causes immediate, strong, involuntary coughing. If you believe someone has aspirated baby oil (or anything else), especially if they are **coughing** or having other **respiratory symptoms**, seek **medical attention** right away.

Common ingredients

Mineral oil is not toxic but many parents prefer more "natural" fruit or vegetable oils.

Mineral oil, the main ingredient in Johnson's® Baby Oil, is a by-product of petroleum distillation, the process of refining crude oil into products such as gasoline and kerosene.

Very pure mineral oil may be classified as **food grade** and has been used orally as an emollient laxative for many years. It is not absorbed into the body and works by softening the stool and coating it so it doesn't dry out. Mineral oil is not toxic when swallowed, but breathing it into the lungs can cause **lipid pneumonia**, which makes breathing difficult and can leave vital organs starved for oxygen. Oprah Winfrey did a segment on her popular television show in 2003 about a child who died after aspirating baby oil. This tragedy led to a new requirement for child-resistant packaging.

Like other petroleum-based products, mineral oil coats the skin but does not penetrate it, so while it may form a barrier to hold moisture in or out, it doesn't actually moisturize the skin.

Mineral oil biodegrades poorly and is made from a nonrenewable resource, and some baby oils are made with fruit and vegetable oils instead.

Sometimes added to baby oil

Aloe vera gel is a traditional treatment for burns and other skin problems, although research into its healing properties has been inconclusive. Aloe vera is a perennial succulent native to Africa and the Arabian Peninsula but grown worldwide, often as a potted plant. Processed aloe gel is sold in many stores and it can be taken directly from the plant by cutting open the thick, spiky leaves.

Vitamin E is actually a group of eight fat-soluble compounds with known antioxidant properties. One compound, alpha-tocopherol, has been found to be involved in a number of human biological processes including immune system function, production of red blood cells and utilization of vitamin K. Research suggests vitamin E protects skin from sun damage, but it must be stabilized to maintain its effectiveness in personal care products. Nuts, seeds and vegetable oils are good dietary sources of vitamin E.

Shea butter is derived from the fruit of the shea tree, which grows in several countries of the African savannah. The green fruit is similar in size and shape to limes, but has a hard seed like an avocado. The sweet pulp is an important source of nutrition when other food is scarce. The fatty butter extracted from the shea fruit kernel is used for cooking and exported for use in food and personal care products. Shea butter composition varies according to environmental conditions and processing methods but it is known to have anti-oxidant, anti-inflammatory and possibly anti-aging properties.

shea fruit

 Make your own baby oil

You can use any food grade vegetable or fruit oil on your baby's skin. You can use one oil at a time, or create your own mixture. Commonly used oils include:

- » Coconut oil
- » Almond oil
- » Olive oil
- » Apricot kernel oil
- » Peach kernel oil

You may also add a few drops of lavender oil or vitamin E, or simmer lavender flowers in the oil (strain and cool before using). Don't use oil on broken skin or open sores.

Batteries

How toxic: Not toxic to toxic

Mouth	**Skin**	**Eyes**	**Inhalation**
Leaked contents may be irritating	*Leaked contents may be irritating*	*Leaked contents may be irritating*	*Not expected*
▼	▼	▼	
Rinse mouth	Wash affected area	Irrigate	

What to expect

Residue that has leaked from inside a battery may be irritating but significant injury is not expected.

Swallowed button batteries usually pass without problems but they require monitoring; see below for more information.

Warning

Button (disc) batteries may become lodged in the esophagus and cause severe injury. Medical attention is required for a known or suspected button battery ingestion even if there are no symptoms.

As difficult as it must be, people do sometimes intentionally swallow cylindrical AAA or even AA batteries. Far more common, however, are accidental ingestions of round button batteries by curious children or adults with dementia.

Aside from the obvious choking hazard, button batteries are worrisome because they have been known to stick to the wall of the esophagus, where they may leak and cause severe injury. Coughing, drooling and pain are obvious symptoms that this is occurring, but it is also possible for there to be no symptoms at first.

For this reason every button battery ingestion, whether confirmed or only suspected, requires a localizing X-ray to ensure it has passed safely to the stomach. If the battery is found to be in the esophagus it will be removed by endoscopy.

As with other foreign bodies, once a battery has made it to the stomach it is unlikely to cause problems. However, if the battery is large enough to have trouble leaving the stomach, intervention may be necessary.

Once an ingestion has been confirmed by X-ray the stool must be examined until the battery passes. This usually happens within three days but could take up to two weeks.

Before leaving the emergency room ask for a **hat**—a plastic device that you can place over the toilet to collect stool. You can also use plastic wrap stretched across the toilet with a little slack in the middle, but the hat is easier.

If the battery isn't seen within an agreed-upon amount of time another X-ray will be needed to see where it is. Even with diligent monitoring a small battery may pass unnoticed.

How batteries work

Electricity, in simplest terms, is a flow of electrons. When you plug an appliance into a wall receptacle, electrons flow from the outlet into one prong of the plug, through the appliance and back into the wall through the other prong.

A battery takes the place of the wall outlet. Electrons flow from the negative side of the battery, through the powered appliance and into the positive side of the battery. When all the available electrons have moved from the negative side to the positive side, the battery is depleted (dead). When a rechargeable battery is plugged into a charger, the flow of electrons is reversed and they return to the negative side of the battery.

Some early rechargeable batteries suffered a **memory effect** in which they lost capacity if they were recharged before running down completely, but this isn't a problem with today's batteries. All batteries have a limited lifespan, however, and will eventually lose the ability to recharge.

Disposing of batteries

The US and EU have phased out the use of mercury in single-use, or primary, batteries. Alkaline and carbon-zinc primary batteries are now considered safe to toss with regular household trash. Safe doesn't mean desirable; batteries dumped in landfills will still leak their contents into the ground, and their casings will never degrade.

Rechargeable, or secondary, batteries contain heavy metals and are considered hazardous waste. They should never be thrown in with the regular trash.

Laws and regulations regarding disposal and recycling of batteries vary and you should consult your waste disposal company or local environmental office for more information. Currently California is the only US state that requires **all batteries** to be treated as hazardous waste.

Find more info at www.earth911.com.

Lithium battery dangers

Lithium ion batteries have become the standard for consumer electronics like cell phones, tablets and laptops because they are very energy dense, packing a lot of power into a small space. They are also rechargeable and don't experience the memory effect.

However, the energy density of lithium ion batteries also means that damage, manufacturing imperfections or exposure to heat can cause them to burst into flames without warning.

This is rare but when it happens the consequences can be catastrophic. In 2010 lithium ion batteries being transported in a UPS plane caught fire, destroying the plane and killing the crew. It was once believed the missing Malaysia Airlines flight 370 might have been brought down by lithium ion batteries in its cargo hold. And in 2016 a manufacturing defect in Samsung Note 7 smartphone batteries caused some of them to combust spontaneously, leading to a massive recall and a universal prohibition against carrying the phones on planes.

Most airlines now have specific rules about how many lithium ion batteries can be carried on a their planes and how they must be packaged.

Bleach, chlorine

How toxic: Minimally toxic

Mouth	**Skin**	**Eyes**	**Inhalation**
May irritate throat	*May be drying*	*May be irritating*	*May be irritating; see warning below*
▼	▼	▼	▼
Rinse mouth, drink water or milk	Wash affected area	Irrigate	Fresh air

What to expect

Ingestion Mild throat irritation is common. Children may have more severe symptoms, especially with concentrated bleach. Coughing, drooling, pain or difficulty swallowing require medical attention.

Inhalation Fumes that result from mixing bleach with ammonia or acid are sharply irritating to eyes, nose, throat and lungs and may trigger asthma. Breathing steam is very soothing to the respiratory tract.

> ### Warning
> Never mix **bleach** with products containing **ammonia** or any kind of **acid**, as irritating toxic gases will be produced. See below for more information.

Common ingredients

Chlorine bleach has a shelf life of about one year, because it slowly breaks down into water and sodium chloride—basically, salt water.

Sodium hypochlorite, the active ingredient in chlorine bleach, is produced either by combining **chlorine gas** and **sodium hydroxide** (lye) or by passing an electrical current through a solution of water and sodium chloride (table salt). The second method is known as **electrochlorination** and is also the principle behind salt water pools (p. 154).

Household bleaches that contain **6% sodium hypochlorite** have a pH of about 11, which is pretty basic but not extremely corrosive. Concentrated household bleaches contain **8.25% sodium hypochlorite** with a pH of at least 11.5

and may cause burns when swallowed or splashed in the eyes. **Children** are most at risk for burns to the mouth and esophagus.

Sodium chloride (table salt) is a natural component of sodium hypochlorite solutions. Chlorine bleach will, over time, break down into little more than water and sodium chloride.

Sodium hydroxide (lye) helps to maintain alkalinity so the sodium hypochlorite doesn't break down into water and salt too quickly.

Sodium carbonate (washing soda, p. 178) adds alkalinity and works both as a solvent and as a builder (p. 126), trapping minerals like calcium and magnesium.

Sodium dichloroisocyanurate is a compound used with sodium hypochlorite to make bleach crystals. It is inactive when dry but when dissolved in water it releases chlorine.

Mixing bleach & other products

Acids (such as toilet bowl cleaner)

When sodium hypochlorite is dissolved in water, molecular bonds are broken and reformed into sodium hydroxide (lye), hypochlorous acid, hypochlorite ion and **chlorine gas**. The proportion of each depends on the pH of the solution. When chlorine bleach is mixed with an acid, the lower pH produces more chlorine gas, which is released into the air.

Ammonia (including urine)

When bleach and ammonia are mixed, chlorine atoms from the bleach bond with nitrogen atoms from the ammonia and form three different kinds of **chloramines**.

Adding bleach to ammonia is an obvious way to create these poison gases, but sometimes they are mixed accidentally. **Urine** contains ammonia, so pouring bleach into an unflushed toilet or a cat box with a lot of residue can have the same effect.

Chlorine and chloramine gases in highly concentrated form can be used as chemical weapons, but the gases you accidently make at home are more irritating than deadly. Gases are created instantly when the chemicals are mixed and any coughing or burning occurs right away, so don't worry if you only realize your mistake later after reading one of the product labels.

 Emergency water disinfection

Do not use bleach that is scented, color safe, or has added cleaners. If water is cloudy, let it settle and filter it through a clean cloth, paper towel or coffee filter before disinfecting.

» Take a clean dropper from your medicine cabinet or emergency supply kit.

» Use liquid bleach that has been stored at room temperatures for less than one year.

» Refer to the adjacent table to determine the amount of bleach to add. Double the amount of bleach if the water is cloudy, colored or very cold.

» Stir and let stand for 30 minutes. The water should have a slight chlorine odor. If it doesn't, repeat the dosage and let stand for another 15 minutes before use.

» If the chlorine taste is too strong, pour the water back and forth from one clean container to another and let it stand for a few hours.

Volume of water	Amount of 6% bleach	Amount of 8.25% bleach
1 quart/liter	2 drops	2 drops
1 gallon	8 drops	6 drops
2 gallons	16 drops (1/4 teaspoon)	12 drops (1/8 teaspoon)
4 gallons	1/3 teaspoon	1/4 teaspoon
8 gallons	2/3 teaspoon	1/2 teaspoon

Bleach, oxygen

How toxic: Not toxic to minimally toxic

Mouth	**Skin**	**Eyes**	**Inhalation**
May be irritating	*Not likely to irritate*	*May be irritating*	*Not expected (does not have irritating fumes)*
▼	▼	▼	
Rinse mouth	Wash affected area	Irrigate	

What to expect

Liquid oxygen bleaches are slightly acidic whereas granular bleaches are more alkaline. Accidental exposures to household oxygen bleaches are not expected to cause significant injury, but care should be taken and medical evaluation sought for symptoms that persist after washing or irrigation.

Common ingredients

Powdered oxygen bleaches contain compounds that produce hydrogen peroxide when added to water. Liquid oxygen bleaches contain hydrogen peroxide in water, plus additional ingredients to slow the natural decay of the peroxide.

Hydrogen peroxide (p. 118) is kinder to fabrics than chlorine bleach. It also works by breaking molecular bonds in stains that reflect visible light, but hydrogen peroxide doesn't go on to break those bonds in fabric dyes the way hypochlorites can. Hydrogen peroxide is unstable by nature and over time will break down, release its extra oxygen and become just plain water.

Sodium percarbonate combines hydrogen peroxide with **sodium carbonate** (washing soda, p. 178) to make a granular compound. When sodium percarbonate is dissolved in water it reverts to hydrogen peroxide, which serves as the bleach, and sodium carbonate, which alkalinizes the solution and binds minerals in the water. **Sodium perborate** serves the same function but is less environmentally friendly.

Benzenesulfonic acid is a bleach activator. It speeds up chemical reactions, allowing hydrogen peroxide to work as a bleach at lower temperatures and in shorter wash cycles than it otherwise would.

Subtilisin, a **protease**, or enzyme that breaks down proteins, is derived from *Bacillus subtilis* bacteria. It isn't practical for use in liquid bleach but can be added to granular products, where it is coated to keep it from interacting with the bleach before it is dissolved in water.

Stabilizers may be added to liquid oxygen bleaches to slow the hydrogen peroxide's inevitable breakdown. Manufacturers are pretty cagey about the stabilizers they use, but they seem to include various organic acids and nitrogen-containing compounds.

How bleach works

The science of **color** is counterintuitive. When we look at a red apple, it seems to us the apple possesses the quality of redness—but the opposite is true. Light waves of every color hit the apple, and the apple absorbs all of them except those we perceive as red, which it bounces back to our eyes. The apple looks red to us because it repels redness.

Which colors an object or substance absorbs and which it reflects is determined on a molecular level, according to how its electrons interact. Anything that affects that interaction also affects the color.

And that's how bleach works, whether chlorine or color safe: The bleach oxidizes, or steals electrons from, the substance to be bleached, altering the way it absorbs and reflects light.

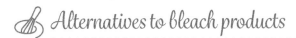 Alternatives to bleach products

Before trying out homemade bleach on anything other than white fabrics, always test for color fastness by dabbing a bit on an inconspicuous area with a cotton swab and rinsing.

Sodium percarbonate, the active ingredient in most granular oxygen bleaches, can be purchased separately and used on its own.

Add ¼ cup to ½ cup per load for general brightening. For yellowed linens and shirts with underarm stains, mix ¼ cup sodium percarbonate per gallon of hot water and soak items until white. Wear gloves if your hands will be in contact with the solution.

Once sodium percarbonate has been dissolved in water it should be used within 5 or 6 hours as it will slowly lose its effectiveness. Never store sodium percarbonate solution in a closed container—the rapid release of oxygen may create enough pressure to rupture the container. It is not recommended for wool or silk.

Hydrogen peroxide (p. 118) can also be used on its own. Use the 3% solution in the brown bottle that you buy from the drug or grocery store; higher concentrations are not necessary and are very dangerous to handle. Pour 1 cup into the washing machine's bleach dispenser, or into the washer drum before adding clothes.

Lemons can be used to whiten yellowed fabrics and underarm stains. Boil water with lemon slices in it and remove from heat. Add items to be whitened and soak for an hour, then launder as usual. You can also pour 1 cup lemon juice into your washing machine's bleach dispenser or add it with the detergent.

Borax (p. 46) reacts with water to form hydrogen peroxide. Add ½ cup to each load of laundry.

Borax

How toxic: Not toxic to toxic

Mouth	**Skin**	**Eyes**	**Inhalation**
May be irritating	*May be irritating*	*May be irritating*	*Not expected*
▼	*See below*	▼	
Rinse mouth	▼	Irrigate	
	Wash affected area		

What to expect

Borax can cause vomiting and diarrhea with a full swallow, but because it is a powder it would be very unusual for someone to take more than a taste of it.

Borax is usually non-irritating to skin but a few children have suffered burns to their hands after playing with borax "slime." Children should be supervised when using borax.

Borax is generally of very low toxicity, but some will find it more irritating than others. Making **slime** with borax is a beloved home and school activity, but there have been reports of children suffering burns to their hands after long play sessions with it.

This is very uncommon and likely to be due to some combination of unusually thin or sensitive skin, prolonged exposure and perhaps mismeasurement of ingredients.

About borax

Borax is a mineral form of **boron**. Most elements are formed as stars are created, merge and die, but boron, like beryllium and lithium, is different. It is formed by **spallation**, a process in which cosmic rays smash into atoms, causing them to split and form new elements.

Like many elements boron does not occur in nature in its pure form. It is always bound with other elements in compounds known collectively as **borates**. Borax, also known as **sodium borate**, is composed of boron, sodium and oxygen.

Borax is mined from dry lake beds. Once it was mined in Tibet and carried along the ancient Silk Road, but now most of the world's borax comes from California. The history of **Death Valley** is wrapped up with borax; it was mined there before the area became a national park. Borax was hauled out on wagons pulled by teams of 20 mules, the origin of the famous **20 Mule Team** brand. Mining has since moved to Boron, California but you can still visit the Furnace Creek Resort in Death Valley and view the ruins of the Harmony Borax Works.

Borax is commonly used as a **laundry booster**. With a pH of 8 it is less alkaline than detergents and hard water. Borax lowers the washwater pH, making detergents more effective. Additionally, borax reacts with water to form **hydrogen peroxide**, a color safe bleach.

Other uses for borax

Insecticide How it works on ants and roaches isn't entirely clear, but it is believed it sabotages their digestive systems. Borax kills slowly, allowing the bugs to carry it back to their nests for others to feed on.

Ants Dissolve ½ cup sugar and 1½ tablespoon borax in 1½ cup hot water. Soak cotton balls in the solution and place where you've seen ants.

Roaches Mix 3 parts borax to 1 part sugar. Sprinkle along baseboards, in cabinets and anywhere roaches might roam.

Drying flowers Mix 1 part borax to 2 parts rolled oats. Spread a layer of the mix over the bottom of a lidded box and arrange flowers to be dried. Carefully add more mix until flowers are covered. Close the box and leave it undisturbed in a warm, dry place for at least a week. Check for dryness and repeat process as needed.

Crystal snowflakes Dissolve 3 tablespoons borax in 8 ounces of very hot water (increase amount as needed, but in the same proportions) in a glass jar. Bend a chenille pipe cleaner into the desired shape. Lay a pencil over the top of the jar and suspend the pipe cleaner by a string or wire so it is entirely immersed in the solution and is not touching the sides or bottom of the jar. Crystals will form on the pipe cleaner as the water cools. If all the borax doesn't crystalize the first time, remove the pipe cleaner, reheat the water, and replace the pipe cleaner.

 *Make your own slime*

Slime without borax

Slime made without borax won't have the same bouncy, solid feel, but it's still fun.

2 cups cornstarch
1 cup hot water

» Place the cornstarch in a bowl. Add food coloring and/or glitter to the water, if desired, and begin slowly pouring it into the cornstarch while stirring or mixing with fingers. Add enough water to reach a consistency you like; it might not be the whole cup. Consistency can be adjusted by adding more water or more cornstarch. Store in an airtight container.

Slime/gak/flubber with borax

4 ounces Elmer's® or similar white glue
½ cup water
1 teaspoon borax

» Add food coloring and/or glitter to the glue, if desired. Dissolve the borax in the water and slowly add to the glue, stirring with a spoon. You may not need to use all of the borax solution. Knead the slime until it is smooth and pliable. Store in an airtight container.

Bubble solutions

How toxic: Not toxic to minimally toxic

Mouth	**Skin**	**Eyes**	**Inhalation**
May upset stomach	*Not toxic*	*May be irritating*	*Not expected*
▼	▼	▼	
Rinse mouth	Wash affected area	Irrigate	

What to expect

Bubble solutions are primarily surfactants, or soaps, with ingredients added to make bubbles stronger. Soaps can be irritating to the stomach and may cause mild vomiting.

Common ingredients

Bubbles formed from soap and water are small and fragile.
Additional ingredients make bubbles bigger and longer lasting.
See page 162 for information on soaps.

Commercial bubble solutions

Glycerol (glycerin, p. 108) is a humectant, or hygroscopic substance, that forms weak bonds with water molecules and keeps them from evaporating too quickly. Its hygroscopic and non-toxic qualities make it a common ingredient in cosmetic, pharmaceutical and food products,

Hydroxyethyl cellulose is derived from cellulose, a vital structural component of plant cell walls. It dissolves in water without clumping and is used as a thickening and gelling agent in a number of products. It strengthens bubble walls.

Citric acid is used as a pH adjuster. The optimal pH for strong bubbles depends on the kind of surfactants (soaps) in the solution. Most are somewhat basic and adjusting the pH makes firmer bubbles even when the solution is diluted.

Homemade bubble solutions

Corn syrup may be substituted for glycerol, which can be synthesized from corn syrup. It is less concentrated than glycerol.

Guar gum is a complex carbohydrate derived from the seed pods of *Cyamopsis tetragonolobus*, a legume native to India and Pakistan. It's a stable thickener that helps soap film stretch, making bigger bubbles.

pH adjusters include citric acid, baking soda/powder, vinegar and cream of tartar.

How bubbles work

Water molecules have a slightly positive charge on one side and a slightly negative charge on the other. Because opposite charges attract, water molecules readily bond with one another.

The molecules bond equally in all directions, except for those on the water's surface. With no other molecules above them, the surface molecules bond more tightly with those below and on either side.

This tight binding creates **surface tension**, a kind of thin film made of water molecules.

The soap molecules in bubble solutions surround the water molecules and form another kind of film, this one made of water sandwiched between layers of soap. Air trapped inside bubbles give the film shape.

Bubbles are spherical no matter what shape they are blown because a sphere requires the least amount of energy to contain the trapped air.

 Make your own bubble solution

Bubble solution with glycerin

6 cups water
1 cup dishwashing liquid
1 tablespoon glycerin

» Mix dishwashing liquid into water gently, without forming bubbles.
» Add glycerin and mix gently.

Bubble solution with corn syrup

6 cups water
1 cup light corn syrup
2 cups dishwashing liquid

» Mix water and corn syrup.
» Add dishwashing liquid and stir gently, without forming bubbles.

Bubble solution with guar gum

2 cups water
¼ cup dishwashing liquid
¼ scant teaspoon guar gum powder
¼ teaspoon baking powder
rubbing alcohol or glycerin

» Cover guar gum powder with rubbing alcohol or glycerin and stir to dissolve.
» Add 1 cup of the water (preferably hot) to the guar gum slurry and stir until completely mixed.
» Stir in the rest of the water.
» Add the dishwashing liquid and mix gently, without forming bubbles.
» Gently stir in the baking powder.
» Allow solution to rest for 15 minutes. (adapted from soapbubblewikia.com)

Calamine lotion

How toxic: Not toxic

Mouth	**Skin**	**Eyes**	**Inhalation**
Not toxic	*Not toxic*	*May be irritating*	*Not expected*
▼	▼	▼	
Rinse mouth	Wash affected area	Irrigate	

What to expect

A full swallow of calamine lotion could cause nausea if the taste is objectionable.

The active ingredients in calamine lotion are present in quantities too small to be toxic.

Common ingredients

The term "calamine" has had many meanings, but currently refers to a combination of zinc oxide and iron oxide.

The term **calamine** was once used for a zinc ore that was later determined to contain zinc carbonate and zinc silicate. Those minerals have since been renamed and calamine now only means the familiar zinc oxide/iron oxide combination.

Zinc oxide (p. 70) has antimicrobial and healing properties and is critical for generating new skin cells to heal wounds and broken skin. It doesn't do much to relieve itching.

Iron oxide is a pigment that gives calamine lotion its familiar pink color. It does not appear to serve any other purpose.

Pramoxine hydrochloride is a local anesthetic that interrupts the transmission of information between nerve cells. leading to numbness that relieves pain and itching.

Bentonite is a clay mineral that is added as a thickener and emulsifier.

Alcohol evaporates quickly, carrying heat away from the skin and causing a distracting cooling sensation.

Camphor, derived from camphor trees or pine trees, binds and activates receptors that react to changes in temperature, producing a cooling sensation that is also slightly numbing.

Phenol, a petroleum derivative once known as carbolic acid, was first used as an antiseptic by British surgeon Joseph Lister in the 1880s. Lister proved post-operative infections were caused by microbes rather than "miasma," or bad air, and could be prevented by cleaning wounds and sterilizing surgical instruments with phenol. Phenol causes temporary, reversible injury to nerves so impulse transmission is blocked. It can also be injected as a nerve block.

Why we itch

The sensation of itching is caused by the stimulation of specific nerve fibers in the skin. Presumably this serves to alert us to something that needs attention, such as an insect that should be removed from the skin. It can also be part of an inflammatory response or allergic reaction, though, in which case it is a side effect from other processes and isn't really helpful.

Scratching activates nearby pain receptors and temporarily overrides the itch message. While this provides some relief from the itching, the brain perceives scratching as pain and responds by releasing serotonin, which stimulates more itching. The result is what's known as the **itch–scratch cycle**.

Overcoming the urge to scratch can be very difficult because, for reasons that are poorly understood, scratching is simultaneously perceived as both painful and pleasurable. Itch remedies are designed to either soothe the underlying inflammation or provide a distraction from the itch sensation.

Other treatments for itching

Colloidal oatmeal is made from oats that have been ground into a fine powder that remains suspended in liquid—a gel, basically. Oats contain **avenanthramides**, which are phenolic alkaloids with proven anti-itch and anti-inflammatory properties.

You can grind whole rolled oats at home in a food processor, blender, grain mill or coffee grinder. Add the resulting powder to a warm bath or make a paste with water and apply directly to itchy skin.

poison ivy

Baking soda has long been recommended for soothing itchy, irritated skin although how it works is not explained. It can also be added to a warm bath or made into a paste.

Hydrocortisone (p. 116) is a corticosteroid that is anti-inflammatory and immunosuppressive, which may be helpful when itching is due to an allergic reaction.

Diphenhydramine (DPH) and other antihistamines block **histamine**, a protein produced when the immune system overreacts to something that in itself is harmless. Antihistamines keep histamine from binding to the receptors that cause itching.

Histamine, however, is also present in the brain, where it is critical to the regulation of wakefulness, appetite, memory and learning. DPH crosses the blood–brain barrier and can interfere with these processes, causing drowsiness and other undesirable side effects.

Diphenhydramine is absorbed through the skin and children can overdose from topical use. Also, ironically, some people become sensitized to DPH and applying it to their skin makes itching worse. For these reasons, diphenhydramine is no longer added to calamine lotion. Topical DPH creams should be used with caution.

Carbon monoxide

How toxic: Toxic to extremely toxic

Mouth	**Skin**	**Eyes**	**Inhalation**
Not expected	*Not expected*	*Not expected*	*Potentially life-threatening* ▼ Fresh air; see below

What to expect

Mild symptoms that resolve immediately upon moving away from the exposure area usually don't require medical care.

Moderate to severe symptoms require medical evaluation even if they seem to be getting better.

Warning
Severe exposure to carbon monoxide (CO)—which is odorless, colorless and tasteless—can cause death or permanent disability. Properly placed CO alarms are critical for household safety.

Symptoms of CO poisoning

Carbon monoxide poisoning can be **acute** (all at once) or **chronic** (low level exposure over time). Symptoms depend on degree and length of exposure and are exacerbated by pre-existing health problems.

Carbon monoxide is colorless and odorless, and because symptoms of CO poisoning are non-specific it's easy to attribute them to more common causes.

Acute symptoms can be **flu-like**, and chronic symptoms can mimic **depression**, **dementia** and a host of other conditions.

Symptoms generally resolve when the CO is cleared from the body, but depending on the severity of the exposure there can be lasting effects.

Symptoms from mildest to most serious include:

» Headache, nausea

» Drowsiness, dizziness

» Confusion, impaired judgment

» Vision changes, vomiting

» Shortness of breath, chest pain

» Rapid pulse and respiratory rate

» Loss of consciousness, seizures

» Coma, respiratory failure, death

If you suspect carbon monoxide poisoning, leave your home immediately and call 911.

About carbon monoxide

Combustion, or burning, is a chemical process that gives off heat and light as molecular bonds are broken and reformed. The fuels we burn contain **carbon**, and during combustion carbon atoms combine with oxygen atoms to form **carbon dioxide** (CO_2; one carbon atom and two oxygen atoms) and **carbon monoxide** (CO; one carbon atom and one oxygen atom), both of which are released into the air we breathe.

When oxygen is plentiful combustion forms mostly CO_2 with just small amounts of CO. But if there is an **inadequate supply of oxygen**, increasing amounts of CO will be formed.

Carbon dioxide is a greenhouse gas and hazardous on a global level, but on a personal level it's usually harmless (dry ice, page 76, is an exception). Our own cells produce CO_2 as a normal metabolic byproduct and our **red blood cells** (RBCs) carry it away to our lungs, where we exhale it. The system works perfectly, with the RBCs off-loading CO_2 in the lungs and picking up oxygen to carry back to the cells.

Carbon monoxide is different. It also binds to RBCs, but much more tenaciously than either CO_2 or oxygen. As you breathe in CO, RBCs become saturated and because they cannot swap out CO for O2, cells become oxygen-starved and may begin to die.

The first critical action after CO exposure is to get away from the source and get to **fresh air**. First responders or hospital staff will next provide **oxygen** at atmospheric pressure. More severe poisoning is treated in a **hyperbaric** oxygen chamber, where oxygen is supplied under increased pressure to more quickly displace CO.

How to prevent CO poisoning

As long as a fuel source has an adequate supply of oxygen, it will convert mostly to CO_2. If there's not enough oxygen, though, the carbon in the fuel will form more CO.

» Have your **gas** or **oil furnace** and **gas water heater** professionally serviced every year. You can have a life-threatening problem without noticing any difference in performance.

» Inspect your **chimney and firebox** each year for cracks, leaks and soot buildup.

» Never use **hibachis, barbeques or camp stoves** inside the house (or any enclosed space). They will quickly use up available oxygen and replace it with carbon monoxide.

» Never put aluminum foil over **vent holes** on the bottom of a gas oven.

» Never use a **gas oven to heat** your house. A normally functioning oven already leaks some carbon monoxide into your home. With the flame turned up and the door left open, the oven will rapidly deplete oxygen in the room and begin producing increasing amounts of carbon monoxide.

» Avoid letting your **car idle** inside the garage, especially if the garage is attached to the house.

» Install and use **portable generators** only in well-ventilated outdoor areas at least 20 feet from your home.

» Install **CO detectors** on each level of your home, especially near sleeping areas. Each detector should be at least 15 feet from any fuel-burning appliance to avoid false alarms.

Cat box litter

How toxic: Not toxic

Mouth	Skin	Eyes	Inhalation
Not toxic	*Not toxic*	*Not expected*	*Not expected*
▼	▼		
Rinse mouth	Wash affected area		

What to expect

Cat box litter is not toxic when ingested and rarely poses a choking hazard.
Clumping litter could form a GI obstruction, but this is extremely unlikely.

Soiled litter carries a small risk of illness due to feces (p. 80) and urine (p. 176).
Cat feces may also transmit toxoplasmosis; see opposite page for more.

Common ingredients

Cat litter is made from inert, non-toxic materials, and
even ingestion of soiled cat litter is unlikely to cause illness.

"**Kitty Litter**" is a brand name for a product invented by Ed Lowe, a Michigan man who got the idea in 1947 to try Fuller's earth—clay mineral compounds that absorb liquids, oils and odors—in cat boxes. Before Kitty Litter people made do with cat box fillers like sand, ashes and newspaper.

Bentonite is a clay mineral that absorbs water and odors and has been the standard for cat litter for decades. Bentonite clumps when wet and stays clumped, leading some cat owners to fear their cat will ingest it and suffer an intestinal blockage. There's no evidence (other than anecdotal) that this is a danger; in fact, some humans intentionally ingest bentonite in the belief it will "detoxify" their GI tract.

Zeolites are porous aluminum silicate mineral compounds that form naturally in volcanic rock and alkaline sediment. Each variety of zeolite has pores of a uniform size, and synthetic zeolites are designed to have pores of specific sizes for specific applications. In cat litter zeolites like **mordenite** adsorb both water and ammonia, the compound that gives cat urine its characteristic smell.

Silicon dioxide is better known as **silica gel**. It's porous like zeolites. See page 158 for more about silica gel.

Cristobalite is a lighter, less dense form of quartz, which is a crystalline form of silicon dioxide.

Perlite is a unique aluminum silicate sometimes referred to as **volcanic popcorn**. In its natural form it's hydrated, which means water is trapped inside its crystals. When crude perlite is ground and then heated to vaporize the water, it explodes into light, porous particles up to 20 times their original size. Commonly used as a soil amendment, perlite works in cat litter the way other silicates do, trapping water and other molecules in its pores.

Cedar, pine, corn, grass and **wheat** are all offered as biodegradable and sometimes flushable (with care) "natural" alternatives to traditional clay litter. Manufacturers tout their superior clumping and odor control properties, but offer no explanation for how they "trap odor deep inside."

Alternatives to cat litter

» Chicken scratch or feed

» Equine bedding pellets

» Perlite

» Shredded paper

» Grass clippings

» Peanut shells

» Sand

Cat boxes and toxoplasmosis

Toxoplasmosis is caused by a protozoa called *Toxoplasma gondii*. It's a common pathogen that can be transmitted through infected, undercooked meats.

Most people who contract toxoplasmosis have no noticeable symptoms, but it can cause severe illness in those with **compromised immune systems**.

It is also of concern for **pregnant women** as it can cross the placenta and infect the fetus, leading to eye or nervous system problems long after birth.

Cats can pick up *Toxoplasma* by eating infected rodents, birds or other small animals. They then shed the protozoa in their feces in an encapsulated form called **oocysts**. The oocysts become activated within 1 to 5 days after being passed.

Pregnant women are advised to avoid cleaning cat boxes if possible. If they can't avoid this task they should **wear gloves** while scooping or cleaning the box and wash well afterwards.

Because the oocysts need a day or more to become infectious it is important to **remove feces daily**.

Make your own cat box litter from paper

» Shred paper.

» If using newspaper you can remove some ink by soaking it in water with a small amount of liquid dish soap and rinsing well.

» Sprinkle wet paper with baking soda and knead well to distribute.

» Squeeze out excess water and spread wet paper clumps to dry.

CFLs (compact fluorescent lamps)

How toxic: Not toxic to minimally toxic

Mouth	**Skin**	**Eyes**	**Inhalation**
Not toxic	*Not toxic*	*May be irritating*	*Fumes are toxic when heated*
▼	▼	▼	▼
Rinse mouth	Wash affected area	Irrigate	Fresh air

What to expect

Fluorescent bulbs are lined with rare earth mineral powders that may be irritating but not damaging to the eyes.
Exposure to broken glass should be treated like any other foreign body.

A broken fluorescent bulb should be handled with care but is not dangerous.
The greatest concern with mercury in CFLs is that improper disposal adds to environmental accumulation.

Incandescent light bulbs work by running electricity through a metal wire called a filament. The filament gets so hot it glows, but the light it gives off is just a byproduct of the heat it generates. In fact, 90% of the energy that goes into an incandescent bulb goes to producing heat, leaving just 10% for producing light. This is why incandescent bulbs can be used for egg incubators and play ovens.

Fluorescent bulbs are lined with a mixture of rare earth minerals such as barium aluminate and calcium tungstate, and filled with argon or xenon gas and a drop of **elemental mercury**. When electricity runs through the bulb the mercury vaporizes, ionizes and emits UV rays, which the rare earth mix converts to visible light. (It's similar to the way white clothing glows under the UV rays from a black light.) It takes a relatively small amount of energy to generate light this way and very little is lost to heat.

When a fluorescent bulb is broken, mercury is released. If the bulb breaks when it isn't in use the mercury will be in liquid form, just as it is in a mercury thermometer (p. 172). **Liquid mercury is not dangerous as long as it's cleaned up properly**, and the amount in a fluorescent light fixture is a tiny fraction of the amount in a thermometer.

If the bulb breaks while it is in use, the mercury will be at least partially in vapor form and that makes it more hazardous, although the amount is still quite small.

Avoid using CFLs in children's bedrooms or anywhere they are prone to getting broken.

Cleaning up a broken CFL

Cleanup involves minimizing the amount of mercury in the air, followed by proper disposal.

These instructions are provided by the US Environmental Protection Agency (EPA).

. . . .

Before Cleanup

» Have people and pets leave the room.

» Air out the room for 5 to 10 minutes by opening a window or door to the outside.

» Shut off the central forced air heating or air conditioning system, if you have one.

» Collect materials needed to clean up broken bulb:

- stiff paper or cardboard

- sticky tape

- damp paper towels or disposable wet wipes (for hard surfaces)

- a glass jar with a metal lid or a sealable plastic bag

During Cleanup

» DO NOT VACUUM. Vacuuming is not recommended unless broken glass remains after all other cleanup steps have been taken. Vacuuming could spread mercury-containing powder or mercury vapor.

» Be thorough in collecting broken glass and visible powder. Scoop up glass fragments and powder using stiff paper or cardboard. Use sticky tape, such as duct tape, to pick up any remaining small glass fragments and powder. Place the used tape in the glass jar or plastic bag.

» Place cleanup materials in a sealable container.

After Cleanup

» Promptly place all bulb debris and cleanup materials, including vacuum cleaner bags, outdoors in a trash container or protected area until materials can be disposed of. Avoid leaving any bulb fragments or cleanup materials indoors.

» Check with your local government about disposal requirements in your area, because some localities require fluorescent bulbs (broken or unbroken) be taken to a local recycling center. If there is no such requirement in your area, you can dispose of the materials with your regular household trash.

» If practical, continue to air out the room where the bulb was broken and leave the heating/air conditioning system off for several hours.

Chalk

How toxic: Not toxic

Mouth	Skin	Eyes	Inhalation
Not toxic	*Not toxic*	*Not expected*	*Low-dust chalk may contain casein, a milk protein; see below for more*
▼	▼		
Rinse mouth	Wash affected area		

What to expect

Chalk is generally non-toxic although low-dust chalks may contain casein, which can cause problems for those with severe milk allergies. Old cue chalk may contain lead.

Common ingredients

Most chalks are calcium-based and some are made of the same active ingredient found in dietary supplements and chewable antacids.

Calcium carbonate chalk was formed millions of years ago as plankton called coccolithophores died and their calcium-rich exoskeletons rained down on ocean floors. Time, pressure and heat transform calcium carbonate first into **limestone** and then into **marble**. The **White Cliffs of Dover** are made of this kind of chalk, indicating Britain was once the bottom of a deep sea.

Calcium carbonate is used as a **dietary supplement** because it contains more elemental calcium, which is essential for healthy bones as well as muscle and nerve function, than other calcium compounds. Calcium carbonate is used as an **antacid** because it reacts with hydrochloric acid in the stomach to produce carbon dioxide, water and calcium chloride, a neutral salt.

Chalk made from calcium carbonate is **extruded**, or forced through a tube to shape it, and is dense and hard. Low-dust chalks are primarily calcium carbonate.

Calcium sulfate, or **gypsum**, was formed on seabeds in the same way as calcium carbonate, but through further geological processes it combined with sulfate ions and collected in bodies of salt water. The **White Sands National Monument** in New Mexico is is an enormous gypsum dunefield that was once the floor of an ancient lake. The presence of gypsum on **Mars** indicates there has been water there.

Calcium sulfate with a very fine grain is known as **alabaster**, while coarse-grained calcium sulfate is partially dehydrated and made into **plaster of Paris**. In addition to its wide use in making chalk and concrete, calcium sulfate is used as a water hardener in **beer** brewing and as a coagulant for **tofu**. Chalk made from calcium sulfate is **molded** rather than extruded and is soft and lightweight.

Casein, the primary protein in milk, is used in some low-dust chalks. All chalks emit particles when used, but low-dust, anti-dust or dustless chalks are formulated so the particles drop out of the air and stay close to the chalkboard, rather than floating around the room. Some particles will still escape, however, and casein in chalk has been found to cause problems for children with **milk allergies**.

Silica (p. 158) and **aluminum oxide** are common ingredients in **cue chalk**, used to increase friction between the tips of cue sticks and billiard balls, although at least one brand utilizes volcanic rock. In the past some brands contained **lead**; new cue chalk made in the US is unlikely to contain lead now, but chalk from China and chalk of unknown age and provenance should be handled with care.

Magnesium carbonate is used by gymnasts, weightlifters, rock climbers and other athletes to **absorb sweat** from their hands and help them maintain their grip on equipment. It is better suited to the purpose than calcium chalks because unlike them it does not dissolve in water. It can be drying to hands, though, and some products have essential oils or other ingredients added to protect skin.

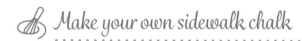

Make your own sidewalk chalk

Plaster of Paris

1 cup plaster of Paris
¾ cup water
Powdered tempera paint or food coloring

» Mix well and pour into a plastic food storage bag. Clip one corner and squeeze into candy molds, ice cube trays, wax-paper lined toilet paper rolls or other molds. Allow to dry completely.

Cornstarch

1 cup cornstarch
1 cup water
Food coloring

» Mix well and spoon into paper towel or toilet paper tubes that have been lined with waxed paper and sealed on one end. Allow to dry completely.

Eggshells

10 to 12 eggshells, dried and crushed into fine powder
2 teaspoons flour
4 teaspoons water
Food coloring

» Mix well. Press into mold or roll into stick. Allow to dry completely.

Citronella tiki torch fuel

How toxic: Not toxic unless aspirated

Mouth	Skin	Eyes	Inhalation
Not toxic	*Not toxic*	*May be irritating*	*Not expected but see aspiration warning p. 38*
▼	▼	▼	
Rinse mouth	Wash affected area	Irrigate	

What to expect

Citronella oil is essentially non-toxic, however it may irritate eyes. Sensitivity reactions are not common but may occur. Cedar oil is not known to cause sensitivity and is approved as a food additive. Citronella tiki torch fuel may have a mineral oil base; see page 38 for information about the dangers of mineral oil aspiration.

Common ingredients

Tiki torches create a nice backyard ambience but do little to keep mosquitoes at bay. A better strategy is to create an unfavorable environment for infestation.

Tiki torch fuel is a clear, yellowish fluid that looks a lot like apple juice. It's a good idea to store it well out of sight of children and others who might mistake it for something good to drink.

Mineral oil is the most common fuel for tiki torches. It is generally not toxic when swallowed but the kind found in torch fuel will not be food grade. Mineral oil is most dangerous when **aspirated**, or breathed into the lungs. This topic is covered more extensively in the entry for baby oil (p. 38).

Citronella oil is steam-distilled from *Cymbopogon nardus* and its derivative *C. winterianus*, grasses in the same family as culinary lemongrass. *C. nardus* is commonly known as **citronella grass**.

Citronella grass is native to Southeast Asia and is grown commercially in Sri Lanka, India, Myanmar, Indonesia and Java. It's grown ornamentally as a perennial in USDA zones 10 to 12 and as an annual elsewhere. It's often grown in containers to keep it from freezing in winter and from overgrowing other garden plants.

Cedar oil is actually distilled from juniper and cypress woods, rather than cedar. Most of the world's cedar oil is produced in China. In the US the oil is often obtained from trees that are being harvested for timber. Like many essential oils, cedar oil is used for its antimicrobial and insecticidal properties as well as for its fragrance.

Other hydrocarbons Tiki fuels may contain proprietary blends of a variety of petroleum derivatives, including paraffin and kerosene. In all cases their potential toxicity is the same as mineral oil.

About DIY tiki torch fuel

Recipes abound for making tiki torch fuel at home by mixing vegetable oils with essential oils that are purported to have bug-repellent properties. These recipes are not included here due to the danger inherent in setting vegetable oils on fire.

Controlling backyard mosquitoes

No standing water Mosquitoes lay their eggs on anything holding water, no matter how small. They attach the eggs to the sides of the container itself, where they will adhere until hatched or physically removed, and where they are impervious to weather and changes in water level.

If you must store water outside, keep it tightly covered. Vases, pet bowls, bird baths, pool covers and anything else that collects water should be emptied and scrubbed once per week.

Run a fan Mosquitoes are weak flyers and a steady breeze is often all that is needed to keep them away.

Wear tightly woven fabrics Synthetic fibers, especially those made for technical athletic wear and to offer protection from UV rays, are harder for mosquitoes to bite through.

Wear light-colored clothing Mosquitoes hunt close to the ground and during daylight hours they are attracted to human shapes that contrast with the sky above.

Make use of plants There are some plants known to repel mosquitoes, but their oils need to be released into the air to have any effect. Rosemary and sage can be added to the fire pit or barbeque to make repellent smoke. Basil, lavender, catnip and peppermint leaves can be crushed and rubbed on skin.

Attract bats Their taste for mosquitoes may be exaggerated, but bats will eat mosquitoes along with other flying insects. They may be especially likely to capture females full from a blood meal. Bat boxes, similar to bird boxes, can be bought or built and attached to trees.

DEET & other mosquito repellents

How toxic: Not toxic to toxic

Mouth	**Skin**	**Eyes**	**Inhalation**
Not toxic	*May be irritating*	*May be irritating*	*Toxic when abused*
▼	▼	▼	▼
Rinse mouth	Wash affected area	Irrigate	See page 19

What to expect

A taste of DEET or other repellent may be unpleasant but symptoms are not expected. Many sprays contain alcohol as a solvent.

DEET causes skin irritation in some people but this is more likely after repeated exposure.

Common ingredients

DEET has been the gold standard in tick and mosquito repellency for decades, but there are numerous effective alternatives, some based on naturally occuring plant pesticides.

DEET was developed in the 1940s for use by the US Army, and as a repellent is highly effective against mosquitoes, ticks and many other biting insects. It is believed that DEET both interferes with insects' ability to locate hosts and actually offends them with its smell. Effectiveness appears to plateau at a 50% concentration; higher concentrations don't work better and may be more irritating. Clothing can be treated with DEET but it must be reapplied after laundering. It is known to damage some plastics and synthetic fabrics. While DEET is an extremely effective repellent, there have long been concerns about its potential toxicity (see opposite page) and the search for alternatives is ongoing.

Picaridin/icaridin is a synthetic form of **piperine**, an oleoresin that gives black pepper its bite and has a number of possible therapeutic uses. Developed as an alternative to DEET, picaridin has no unpleasant odor and does not damage fabrics. Some people have experienced skin irritation with picaridin products but this is very uncommon.

IR3535 (Insect Repellent 3535) is a synthetic form of the amino acid **beta-alanine** that is entirely non-toxic and causes no side effects. It's believed to interfere with insects' odor and taste receptors. While it repels ticks and most mosquitos very well, it is not as effective as DEET against the mosquito that carries malaria.

2-undecanone, also known as methyl nonyl ketone, occurs naturally in numerous plants including cloves, tomatoes and other fruits and berries, as well as palm and soy oils. Extracted from tomato plants, oil of the rue plant or synthesized in the lab, it's used in small amounts in perfumery and food flavoring and in larger amounts as an insect and animal repellent. It may cause some mild irritation but is considered to be of very low toxicity.

Oil of lemon eucalyptus (OLE) is extracted from the Australian **gum eucalyptus** tree. The active repellent ingredient in OLE is p-menthane 3,8-diol (PMD), which is effective but not long-lasting. It is not the same as lemon eucalyptus oil, which is distilled from leaves and twigs of the lemon eucalyptus tree, contains only trace amounts of PMD and is not effective as a bug repellent.

Permethrin is a synthetic form of a chemical found in chrysanthemums. You can buy spray intended for use on clothing that will last through 6 washings; clothing treated with permethrin by the manufacturer is made to last for 70 washings. Permethrin kills mosquitoes rather than repelling them and is meant to be used in addition to, not instead of, a topical repellent.

Metofluthrin is a newer pyrethroid (the same class of pesticide as permethrin) that kills mosquitoes on contact. Metofluthrin is used in small devices, some wearable, with battery-operated fans that blow it into the air and create small protective zones. Currently these devices are only meant for outdoor use.

Essential oils and other botanicals such as lemon grass, citronella, peppermint, geraniol, soybean oil and rosemary aren't subject to federal regulations and can be sold as mosquito repellents without evidence that they work. Some botanicals have been shown to have limited, short-lived repellent qualities when applied in high concentrations but so far none stand out as being truly effective.

Is DEET safe?

There have been reports over the years of both children and adults experiencing neurological symptoms, including seizures, after exposure to DEET. The only thing all cases had in common was that symptoms occurred some time after a DEET exposure.

Otherwise the reported cases had little in common. The individuals involved differed in age and gender and they were exposed to DEET in different amounts and concentrations. The length, frequency and routes of exposure varied, as did the time between exposure and onset of symptoms.

In some cases seizures and other symptoms were found to have been caused by previously undiagnosed medical conditions. In no case was DEET determined to have been responsible for the symptoms.

Opinions differ on the toxicity of DEET but its effectiveness as a bug repellent in indisputable. The number of reported cases where DEET may or may not have caused symptoms is extremely small compared to the millions of people who rely on DEET's proven effectiveness every year.

In places where serious tick- and mosquito-borne illness are endemic, DEET's risks are dwarfed by the benefit of protection from those illnesses.

In any case, **picaridin** is considered a highly effective alternative to DEET with little if any known toxicity, so if you're worried about DEET, you have an excellent alternative.

Degreasers

How toxic: Not toxic to minimally toxic

Mouth	**Skin**	**Eyes**	**Inhalation**
May be irritating	*Not toxic*	*May cause injury*	*Not expected*
▼	▼	▼	
Rinse mouth	Wash affected area	Copious irrigation for 30 minutes	

What to expect

Pain or blistering in the mouth is not expected and would require medical attention.
Throat pain or trouble swallowing needs evaluation even if the mouth looks fine.

Eyes should be irrigated for 30 minutes after any degreaser exposure.
Medical evaluation is needed for pain or vision changes after irrigation.

Common ingredients

Degreasers for home use are mostly water—the universal solvent—with small amounts of mildly irritating ingredients. Industrial products may cause severe injury.

Degreasers contain alkalis that break the molecular bonds holding fats and proteins together, turning them to a soapy liquid. In fact, this process is called **saponification** and it's how soap is made (see page 162). As a general rule, degreasers for kitchen use are going to be milder than degreasers for use in the garage.

Surfactants disrupt surface tension and help water molecules interact less with each other and more with other substances. Surfactants also surround oil deposits so they can be wiped or rinsed away. They may cause stomach upset when ingested but are otherwise not toxic.

Lauramine oxide (dodecyldimethylamine oxide) is a versatile surfactant that is derived from coconuts. It is used in a wide variety of consumer products including cosmetics and other personal care items. Lauramine oxide is amphoteric, meaning it acts as either an acid or a base depending on the other substances it interacts with.

Phenoxyisopropanol (propylene glycol phenyl ether) is a solvent that mixes well with water and evaporates very slowly.

Ethanolamines are used as pH adjusters to keep products alkaline, because alkaline substances are best for dissolving oils and grease. They may also have detergent and emulsification properties.

Ethanolamines are incorporated into biological processes in both plant and animal cells. Antihistamines like diphenhydramine (Benadryl®) and doxylamine (Unisom®) are also ethanolamines.

Tetrapotassium pyrophosphate is a builder that bonds with minerals like calcium and magnesium to keep them from interfering with surfactants. It also works as an emulsifier and performs a variety of functions in different food products.

Diethylene glycol monobutyl ether (DGME) is a mutual solvent that can dissolve both water- and oil-based substances so it can all wash away together. It is widely used in many consumer products.

Potassium silicate adds alkalinity. It also has emulsification qualities and helps prevent soil from redepositing on the surface being cleaned.

Sodium hydroxide (lye) is a very strong alkaline and a superior degreaser. Because it is a powerful saponifier it is the most dangerous of all products used for this purpose.

Limonene (orange or lemon oil) is a solvent found in the peels of citrus fruits. Limonene is used as a flavoring for foods and medicines as well as a solvent and pesticide. The limonene molecule is **chiral**, which means it comes in two forms that are mirror opposites of one another: One smells like fruit and is used in consumer products, while the other smells like pine oil and is used for industrial applications.

Make your own degreaser

Citrus vinegar

Fill a jar with clean, pulp-free citrus peels of any kind. (If you don't have enough peels all at once you can collect them in the freezer until you do.) Cover the peels with distilled white vinegar, close the jar and leave out on the counter for one to two weeks. Strain the vinegar into a spray bottle and dilute with an equal amount of water.

White vinegar

Spot clean with undiluted vinegar, or dilute one cup with two or three cups plain water. Don't use vinegar on granite or marble, and use with caution on hardwood floors.

Ammonia

Mix equal parts ammonia (p. 28) and water. Add a few drops of liquid soap or citrus oil if desired. Use in a well-ventilated area and never mix ammonia with bleach (p. 42).

Baking soda paste

Add just enough water to baking soda to form a thick but pliable paste. Rub in with a wet cloth and rinse with plain water.

Deodorants & antiperspirants

How toxic: Not toxic to minimally toxic

Mouth	**Skin**	**Eyes**	**Inhalation**
Not toxic	*Hypersensitivity to aluminum is possible*	*May be irritating*	*Not expected*
▼	▼	▼	
Rinse mouth	Wash affected area	Irrigate	

What to expect

A lick of a roll-on or even a bite out of a solid deodorant stick is not toxic.

Dermal hypersensitivity to aluminum, with itching and irritation, is rare but does occur.

Common ingredients

Deodorants contain antimicrobials to cut down on bacteria and perfumes to cover up odor. Antiperspirants use aluminum salts to plug sweat glands, keeping skin dry.

Aluminum chloride, aluminum chlorohydrate and aluminum zirconium tetrachlorohydrex GLY are all **aluminum salts**. They are thought to dissolve in sweat to form a gel that blocks pores, although another theory is that they diffuse into skin cells, taking water with them so the cells swell and close the pores.

Cyclopentasiloxane, a silicone derivative, has atoms arranged in rings that can grasp active ingredients and deliver them to the skin. It also imparts a smooth, silky feel.

Alum is the common name of **ammonium aluminum sulfate**. Products containing alum, including deodorant **crystals**, cannot be said to be "aluminum free."

Zinc ricinoleate combines zinc oxide (p. 70) with ricinoleic acid, which is derived from **castor beans** (p. 70). How it works isn't entirely understood, but it is thought to capture odor molecules and keep them from reaching your nostrils. It has a special affinity for compounds containing nitrogen and sulfur, which are found in many of the worst underarm offenders.

Peptides are tiny chains of amino acids that are much smaller than proteins. Peptides are purported by manufacturers to control sweating by diffusing into sweat gland cells and plumping them up so they block pores.

Ethanol kills bacteria and is an astringent that tightens pores.

Witch hazel (p. 180) is a gentle astringent.

Essential oils help cover up odor, but some have antimicrobial or astringent properties as well.

Propylene glycol is used as a carrier for active ingredients. It can be a petroleum product but in a "natural" deodorant it is more likely to be derived from **vegetable glycerin**.

Is aluminum toxic?

Aluminum is the most abundant metal on Earth. It is found in nature in over 270 mineral combinations and enters air, water and soil through natural processes as well as being added to food, beverages, cookware, packaging, medications and personal care products.

Because antiperspirants alter a normal biological process (sweating), they are classified as OTC drugs. Just like other OTCs, the aluminum salts in antiperspirants are subject to extensive study and testing before they are approved, and must comply with very specific regulations to ensure safety and effectiveness.

Research has found that less than 0.012% of aluminum in antiperspirants is absorbed through skin before being excreted in urine and feces. Research is ongoing into whether aluminum can accumulate in the body and what that might mean. So far there is no good evidence the aluminum compounds approved for use in antiperspirants pose a danger to health.

It may be possible to ingest a toxic amount of aluminum-containing **antacids**, however, especially if you have kidney disease.

Alzheimer's disease

Clumps of sticky proteins called amyloid plaques and deformed proteins called tangles are found in the brains of people with **Alzheimer's**. Some plaques and tangles have been found to contain aluminum as well as copper, iron and zinc, but we don't know if any of these metals contribute to dementia; it is also possible the disease itself causes them to accumulate.

Cancer

Research to date has established no correlation between aluminum and cancer, or identified any mechanism by which it could cause or contribute to cancer.

 ## Make your own deodorant

There's no effective DIY antiperspirant, but many suggestions for homemade deodorants. You may have to try a few to find one that works for you and doesn't irritate your skin.

Single ingredient

- » Baking soda
- » Witch hazel
- » Vinegar
- » Rubbing alcohol or vodka

Essential oils

Any combination of oils can be added to any recipe, but those most recommended for deodorant purposes include tea tree, peppermint, lavender, lemon and thyme.

Coconut oil deodorant

6 tablespoons coconut oil (or shea butter, or a combination of the two)
4 tablespoons arrowroot or cornstarch
4 tablespoons corn starch
Essential oils as desired

Depilatories (hair removers)

How toxic: Not toxic to toxic

Mouth	**Skin**	**Eyes**	**Inhalation**
May be irritating	*May be irritating*	*May be irritating*	*Not expected*
▼	▼	▼	
Rinse mouth	Wash affected area, irrigate copiously	Irrigate copiously	

What to expect

Depilatories may cause irritation and burns even when used as intended.
Every route of exposure should be treated first by copious irrigation with running water.

After irrigation, injury to skin should be treated like any other burn. Eye pain, vision changes, or any difficulty breathing or swallowing, require immediate medical attention.

Common ingredients

Depilatories dissolve hair with highly alkaline ingredients. Accidental exposures usually cause only mild irritation, but some people suffer first or second degree burns when they intentionally apply these products to their skin.

Hair removal products generally are alkaline with a pH falling between bleach and ammonia. Most people will experience only mild irritation from accidental depilatory exposure, but some may suffer first or second degree burns even when used as directed.

The most important treatment is irrigation with plain water. After copious irrigation, exposed areas should be inspected and treated appropriately.

Thioglycolates are highly alkaline compounds formed by reacting thioglycolic acid with a base. The most common compounds used in depilatories are calcium thioglycolate and potassium thioglycolate. A related compound, ammonium thioglycolate, is used for perms, and sodium thioglycolate is used to remove hair from leather hides. Thioglycolates have distinctly unpleasant odors due to their **sulfur** content, and when they are breaking sulfur bonds in hair the odor is increased. Thioglycolates also break sulfur bonds in skin cells, but skin has fewer of these bonds and depilatories are generally safe when used appropriately.

Calcium hydroxide is calcium oxide (derived from **limestone**) that has been slaked, or mixed with water; another name for it is **slaked lime**. It is found in many products from cement to pickled vegetables.

Sodium hydroxide is also known as **lye**. It was once used for homemade depilatories but this is not recommended!

How depilatories work

Hair is composed of tightly bound strands of a protein called **keratin**. Keratin is also a component of skin, as well as of scales, feathers and horns.

Depilatories dissolve the bonds that hold keratin strands together, turning hair into mush that can easily be rinsed away. They do the same to keratin in the dead cells that make up the outer layer of the skin, and so have an exfoliating effect as well.

Because depilatories dissolve hair just below the surface of the skin, the results can be smoother and longer lasting than shaving.

Depilatories don't penetrate all the way down to the root, though, and don't keep hair from growing back at its normal rate.

Make your own epilatory: Sugaring

Sugaring is actually **epilation**, rather than depilation, as it plucks hair out by the roots rather than dissolving it.

Sugaring paste
2 cups granulated sugar
¼ cup lemon juice
¼ cup water

» Mix all ingredients in a heavy pan.

» Bring to a boil and cook for 5 to 7 minutes, until it is a rich brown color.

» Allow to cool and pour into a glass container.

To use

Cleanse skin gently but well. Dry thoroughly and apply a very light dusting of cornstarch or unmedicated powder (you want to protect the skin but not coat the hair).

Spread the cooled paste in the opposite direction of hair growth and press. Roll an edge of the paste, grasp firmly and pull in the same direction the hair is growing. You can continue to use the same paste until it is no longer effective, then take a fresh scoop.

When finished, wash off any paste remnants with water and a gentle soap. Apply cool compresses as needed.

Treat skin very gently for the next 24 hours—no pools, hot tubs, tanning, heavy workouts or tight fitting clothes. After 24 to 48 hours begin gently exfoliating sugared areas with each shower and moisturize afterward to help prevent ingrown hairs.

Sugaring gel

» Follow instructions for paste, using just 1 cup of sugar.

To use

Spread gel with a dull butter knife in the opposite direction of hair growth, then apply a cloth strip. Grasp edge of strip and pull in the same direction hair is growing. Finish as with paste.

Diaper cream (zinc oxide)

How toxic: Not toxic

Mouth	**Skin**	**Eyes**	**Inhalation**
Not toxic	*Not toxic*	*May be irritating*	*Not expected*
▼	▼	▼	
Rinse mouth	Wash affected area	Irrigate	

What to expect

Zinc oxide creams are not toxic, but some children may gag and vomit from the texture.

Unusually large ingestions could cause mild diarrhea by lubricating the GI tract.

Common ingredients

Diaper creams are intended to protect skin from irritation and heal rashes.
Their creamy texture makes them naturally attractive to curious
babies and toddlers, and do no harm when tasted.

Zinc oxide is the same kind of zinc you will find in vitamins and other foods. Zinc oxide has been used as a topical ointment for thousands of years because it has antimicrobial properties and promotes healing. Zinc is critical to the process of generating new skin cells to heal wounds and broken skin. Zinc supplements can help with wound healing if you are zinc-deficient, but applying zinc directly to the skin that needs it is effective whether the rest of your body needs more zinc or not.

Cod liver oil is taken from the livers of cod, fish of the genus *Gadus* found in the Atlantic and Pacific oceans. Cod liver oil contains small amounts of vitamins A and D (see more on page 24).

Castor oil is derived from the seed of the *Ricinus communis* plant and is processed to remove the deadly **ricin** that is also found in the *Ricinus* seed. The name castor comes from the Latin for beaver, as castor oil first gained renown as a replacement for castoreum, taken from the beaver's perineal glands. (Castoreum is musky and a synthetic version is used in several high-end perfumes.) Castor oil has a great many medicinal and commercial uses because of its high fatty acid content. Once a common laxative, it is often used as a hair and skin moisturizer and is said to promote hair growth.

Lanolin (p. 124), also known as **wool grease**, is a wax secreted by the sebaceous glands of sheep. Lanolin closely resembles the oils our own skin produces and is effective at soothing and moisturizing.

Petrolatum (p. 152), also called petroleum jelly, is derived from petroleum oil. It forms a barrier to protect skin from irritants.

Zinc oxide fumes (metal fume fever)

Although topical creams containing zinc oxide are perfectly safe to use at home, zinc oxide **fumes** can be toxic. This is an occupational hazard for **welders** and others who work with metals that have been **galvanized**, or coated with zinc oxide to prevent rusting.

Inhaling the dust or fumes given off when these metals are cut or heated can cause a condition called **metal fume fever**.

Metal fume fever usually clears when the exposure ends, but anyone having flu-like symptoms after working with galvanized metals should consult their healthcare provider.

Removing zinc oxide cream from fabric

Removing zinc oxide cream from fabrics involves two processes: removing the oil, and removing the zinc oxide stain. Hot water and laundry detergent usually suffices for the oil, and white vinegar will lift the zinc oxide stain.

Removing zinc oxide cream from hair

Getting zinc oxide cream out of hair can be difficult and may take several tries. Remove as much as possible with a fine-toothed comb. Small amounts of residue may wash out with shampoo or a degreasing dish soap. For more stubborn deposits, apply a paste of baking soda and lemon juice or vinegar, then rinse and shampoo again.

 Make your own diaper cream

Coconut oil is purported to have antimicrobial properties and is a popular choice for homemade diaper creams. The simplest way to use it is simply to whip it until it is fluffy, then store it in a jar and use as needed. It is oily, though, and may soak into cloth diapers; melting it over low heat with beeswax and letting it cool before whipping will help.

You can customize your diaper cream by adding small amounts of:

- » vitamin E
- » tea tree oil
- » lavender oil

If you would like a medicated cream you can add:

- » cosmetic-grade zinc oxide powder
- » liquid Maalox®
- » antibiotic ointment
- » antifungal ointment
- » hydrocortisone cream

Diapers (disposable)
How toxic: Not toxic

Mouth	**Skin**	**Eyes**	**Inhalation**
Not toxic	*Not toxic*	*Not expected*	*Not expected*
▼	▼		
Rinse mouth	Wash affected area		

What to expect

The contents of disposable diapers are not toxic but could present a choking hazard for a small child.

Wet diapers are no more toxic than dry ones (see urine, page 176). Ingestion of feces runs a small risk of illness (see page 80).

Common ingredients

Incontinence products for adults use the same materials and technology as disposable diapers for infants.

Disposable diapers have three main parts: A permeable topsheet that goes against the skin and lets moisture through in only one direction, a layer of absorbent material, and a waterproof backsheet that holds everything in.

The topsheet is commonly made of **polypropylene**, but some manufacturers add a layer of **plant-based fibers** to give it a softer feel.

The absorbent core, known in the business as the acquisition and distribution layer, is usually made of a **super absorbent polymer** (more on next page) within a framework of cellulose fibers.

The fibers come from **fluff pulp**, most of which is derived from softwood loblolly pine trees from the southern US. Fluff pulp was once used by itself as the absorbent core for diapers and sanitary napkins, but the introduction of far less bulky super absorbent polymers has allowed the amount of pulp to be reduced. The pulp fibers work like wicks to carry moisture from the upper layer of the diaper deep into the polymer layer where it can be absorbed and retained.

Environmentally minded consumers may look for diapers made with pulp that is **FSC** (Forest Stewardship Council) certified as sustainably harvested, and **TCF** (totally chlorine free) unbleached.

The backsheet is commonly made of **polyethylene**, but some diapers have backsheets made of a combination of polyethylene, polypropylene, **polyester** and/or **cotton**. The purpose of the backsheet is to keep moisture in the diaper from leaking to the outside, but it may be designed to allow **water vapor** to escape so a wet diaper isn't quite so soggy.

About sodium polyacrylate

In the early 1970s the research arm of the US Department of Agriculture (USDA) was trying to come up with a soil amendment that would allow crops to be grown with less water. USDA scientists invented a super absorbent material popularly known as **Super Slurper** that could hold many times its own weight in water. Mixed in with soil, Super Slurper held water in place and released it gradually, so the water was retained rather than quickly evaporating.

Super Slurper was made by combining synthetic materials with corn starch. The USDA began licensing the Super Slurper technology to private companies and the technology began evolving, with corn starch being replaced by other synthetic materials.

The first consumer products made with super absorbent materials were sanitary napkins and adult diapers, but they have since found a wide variety of uses from wound dressings to waste management.

smelly jelly

Uses for polyacrylate beads

It may be possible to recover sodium polyacrylate beads from unused diapers, but you can also buy them at craft stores, where they are more commonly known as *water beads*, *water gel beads* or *hydrogel*. These beads are spherical and available in various sizes and colors.

Non-spherical beads are more commonly called *water crystals*, *water gel crystals* or *water polymer crystals* and can be purchased in bulk from home improvement stores and gardening centers. These kinds of crystals are available in various sizes and also in powder form.

Smelly jelly air freshener

In a vase, dish or decorative jar mix a teaspoon of water beads or crystals, a cup of water, a drop of essential oil, perfume or other scent of your choice, and if desired a drop of food coloring. If using an oil-based scent add a drop of dish soap to help keep the oil dispersed.

Cool packs

Add hydrated water beads or crystals to a pouch made of cotton fabric and sew it shut. Can be used at room temperature or refrigerated. Soak pack in water if it begins to dry out.

Gardening

Add crystals to soil and water well. The crystals will retain the water and release it slowly into the soil. Can be used indoors and outdoors.

Fake snow

Add water to polyacrylate powder to make fake snow that can be dried out and re-used.

Drain openers
How toxic: Toxic to highly toxic

Mouth	**Skin**	**Eyes**	**Inhalation**
May cause significant injury	*May cause significant injury*	*May cause significant injury*	*Fumes may be irritating*
▼	▼	▼	▼
Rinse mouth	Wash affected area	Irrigate for 30 minutes	Fresh air

What to expect

Drain opener exposures can be serious by any route. Immediate medical attention is needed for vomiting, drooling, coughing, or difficulty breathing or swallowing after ingestion; any pain, discomfort or vision changes after eye exposure; or pain or changes in skin that can be seen or felt, even if these symptoms are noticed later.

Warning
A product that fails to clear a clog will be trapped in the drain pipe. Pouring a different product in after it may produce noxious gases or start a chemical reaction hot enough to erupt out of the drain and melt pipes.

Common ingredients

Drain openers are either highly acidic or highly basic, and are designed to liquefy organic matter.

Sodium hydroxide is also known as lye. It is highly alkaline and breaks the molecular bonds that hold fats and proteins together, turning them to soapy liquid in a process known as saponification (p. 162).

Sodium hypochlorite is the chlorine compound used in bleach (p. 42). It oxidizes the cellulose in plant matter.

Surfactants interrupt the bonds that hold water molecules together, reducing surface tension. Like other liquid and gel products, drain openers are composed of small amounts of active agents suspended or dissolved in water, and surfactants help the water penetrate clogs so the other ingredients can get to work. Surfactants also envelop grease and oils as they are broken up so they stay separated.

Sodium bisulfate, also known as monosodium sulfate, is made by buffering sulfuric acid with sodium chloride or sodium hydroxide. It is promoted as a greener or more environmentally friendly drain opener because it is **biodegradable**. Food grade sodium bisulfate is used as a leavening, flavoring and preservative.

Sodium silicate helps protect metal pipes from being corroded by the drain opener's active components. It also thickens gel products and raises pH.

Benzisothiazolinone is an antimicrobial that breaks down **biofilm**, the slimy bacterial residue that accumulates in plumbing.

Enzymes break down organic matter. They work much more slowly than acids, alkalis and oxidizers and generally need to be coupled with one or more of these to help them get started.

Enzymatic mixtures are proprietary and you won't find details on the label, but the kinds of enzymes that may be included are well known. **Amylases** break down cellulose and starches and are derived from *Bacillus subtilis*, which also provides **proteases** that break down proteins. **Lipases** break down fats and may be derived from bacteria, yeasts or animal pancreases. **Pectinases** that break down pectin in plant cell walls are mostly derived from fungi but can also be obtained from bacteria and yeasts. **Cellulases** break down cellulose and are mostly derived from the fungus *Trichoderma reesei* although they can also be found in some bacteria and protozoans.

 ## Alternatives to drain openers

Bathroom

Minimize accumulation of hair with a plastic or wire mesh strainer over the drain opening.

Remove hair from a slowly draining tub or sink with a plastic toothed snare from a home supply store.

Chlorine bleach dissolves hair. Pour 1 cup bleach down the drain, wait an hour or overnight and then run hot water to rinse. This may not work if there is standing water above the clog.

Kitchen

Be forewarned that pouring boiling water down the drain runs the risk of **melting PVC pipes** and connections.

Boiling water alone may be enough to melt accumulated grease. Scoop out any standing water, then pour in a kettle or pot of boiling water. You may need to repeat this a few times, allowing the water to cool and scooping it out again before pouring in the next kettle full.

Baking soda and vinegar react to form carbon dioxide fizz that might loosen a clog but won't dissolve it. The method uses boiling water, though, so may still work. Scoop out any standing water. Pour a cup of baking soda into the drain, followed by a cup of vinegar, then the boiling water. Repeat as needed.

Detergent and boiling water most closely mimics the action of commercial drain openers; the hot water takes the place of the heat-forming chemical reactions of acids, alkalis and oxidizers, and the detergent provides the surfactant to help break up grease and keep it from re-solidifying. Add a few tablespoons of hand dishwashing soap to 2 quarts or liters of boiling water, mix well and pour down the drain. Flush with hot water. As with the other methods you may need to do this more than once to completely clear a stubborn clog.

Dry ice

How toxic: Not toxic to extremely toxic

Mouth	**Skin**	**Eyes**	**Inhalation**
May cause severe injury	*May cause severe injury*	*May cause severe injury*	*May cause asphyxiation*
▼	▼	▼	▼
Rinse mouth	Wash affected area	Irrigate	Fresh air

What to expect

Dry ice is extremely cold and can cause severe burns. Pain or visible injury to mouth, throat, skin or eyes after direct contact require immediate medical care.

Carbon dioxide displaces oxygen in the air. Symptoms from excessive inhalation such as headache, dizziness and confusion require immediate medical care.

Dry ice is frozen **carbon dioxide** (CO2) that slowly sublimates, or changes directly from solid to gas, rather than melting into a liquid. This is because carbon dioxide molecules are nonpolar and have no particular attraction to one another; the temperature must be extremely low to get them to congregate into a solid form, and they readily fly apart into vapor as they are warmed by contact with air.

Small amounts of carbon dioxide are always present in air, but the quantity given off by dry ice can be **suffocating** in an enclosed space and it should be stored and used only in a well-ventilated area.

It should never be stored in an **airtight** container for the same reason; enough pressure can build up to cause the container to **explode**.

With a surface temperatures of -109 F (-79 C), dry ice can cause severe **burns** and should never be ingested or handled with bare hands.

Uses for dry ice

Flash freezing Place dry ice in the bottom of an insulated cooler. Arrange food on a metal baking sheet, lay it on top of the ice and close the cooler lid. Once frozen, transfer food to freezer bags or other appropriate freezer containers.

Fumigation of grains and nuts Place ¼ pound to ½ pound dry ice in the bottom of a 5-gallon bucket and pour dry food over it. Stretch plastic wrap over the top and secure with a large rubber band. Poke a small hole in the plastic and set bucket aside. Once the dry ice completely evaporates (and not before!), place airtight lid over the plastic, sealing edges with duct tape if desired.

Halloween drinks Dry ice can be placed directly in a bowl of punch or other drink to make fog rise up out of it, as long as it is deep enough to keep anyone from trying to touch it. Otherwise, place dry ice in hot water in a large bowl and place the punch bowl over it so the fog rises around it.

Epsom salt

How toxic: Not toxic to minimally toxic

Mouth	**Skin**	**Eyes**	**Inhalation**
May cause diarrhea	*Not toxic*	*May be irritating*	*Not expected*
▼	▼	▼	
Rinse mouth	Wash affected area	Irrigate	

What to expect

A taste of Epsom salt is not toxic. Epsom salt may be used as a laxative under medical supervision.

Excessive use of Epsom salt or any other magnesium compound can cause serious illness.

Epsom salt is the common name for the mineral compound **magnesium sulfate**. It occurs naturally in two forms, **epsomite** and **kieserite**, that differ only in the amount of water each contains. It is named after the English spa town Epsom, a popular 18th century destination for those who wished to drink its famous water. Contemporary accounts report the water was valued for its **laxative** effects; visitors would drink as much as they could and then go find a place in the shrubbery to enjoy the results.

Only 20% to 30% of Epsom salt's magnesium is absorbed when it is ingested and systemic effects are not expected from an accidental exposure. Massive ingestion and large chronic ingestions may cause serious **hypermagnesemia**, and even small doses may be problematic for those with kidney disease.

There is no scientific justification for claims that ingesting or soaking in Epsom salt eases pain, regulates blood sugar, improves circulation or eliminates toxins.

 How to make Epsom salt crystals

½ cup hot tap water
½ cup Epsom salt
Food coloring (optional)

» Dissolve the Epsom salt in the water; this may take a couple of minutes of stirring. Don't worry if a little salt remains undissolved. Add food coloring if using.

» Pour into a jar with a small piece of sponge to give the crystals a place to start forming.

» Put the jar in the refrigerator and leave undisturbed overnight (up to a week for larger crystals).

» In the morning carefully pour off the leftover water.

Fabric softeners

How toxic: Not toxic

Mouth	**Skin**	**Eyes**	**Inhalation**
Not toxic	*Not toxic*	*May be irritating*	*Not expected*
▼	▼	▼	
Rinse mouth	Wash affected area	Irrigate	

What to expect

Fabric softeners may smell nice but they don't taste very good, and while they could be mildly irritating to the throat and stomach a large ingestion is very unlikely.

A single episode of vomiting might occur but this would likely be due to the taste and texture. Fabric softeners may be mildly irritating to eyes.

Common ingredients

In the early 1900s mixtures of oil and soap were used to coat mass-produced cotton textiles after they were roughed up by harsh dyeing processes. In time more effective softeners were developed and by the 1960s they were being marketed for home use.

Diethyl ester dimethyl ammonium chloride is a cationic surfactant known as a **quaternary ammonium compound**, or quat. Quat molecules have positively charged heads that adhere to fabric and fatty tails that stand up away from it, separating and smoothing its fibers and giving it an overall soft feel.

Quats reduce static cling by equalizing electrical charges between unlike fabrics and lubricating them to lessen friction. The drawback to using quats in fabric softeners is that the way they attach to fibers can interfere with the fabric's intended purposes (see next page for more).

Polydimethylsiloxane (PDMS), also known as **dimethicone**, is a silicone polymer. Polymers are chains of repeating molecules; when PDMS chains are short it's a liquid, but when they are long it's solid.

PDMS gives Silly Putty® its stretchy, bouncy character and makes Kinetic Sand® moldable. It's widely used in household and personal care products for its lubricating and anti-foam properties.

Its function in fabric softeners is very similar to that of diethyl ester dimethyl ammonium chloride, except that for reasons that are not entirely understood it doesn't interfere with a fabric's absorbency.

Dipalmitoylethyl hydroxyethylmonium methosulfate is a quaternary ammonium compound that can be embedded in small pieces of polyester fabric to make dryer sheets.

Fabric softeners and flame resistant clothing

Your fabric softener label may warn against using it on children's sleepwear, but whether or not the warning is needed is somewhat uncertain.

Flame resistant clothing is either made from polyester that is **inherently** flame resistant, or from fabric that has water-insoluble polymers **bonded** to the fibers.

Children's sleepwear nowadays is seldom made of treated fabric; it is usually made either of polyester or of untreated **cotton** that is designed to **fit snugly**. Tight-fitting clothing is less likely to stray onto an open flame and leaves little space between fabric and skin for fire-feeding oxygen.

Clothing manufacturers don't say why fabric softeners shouldn't be used. One theory is that the residue they deposit could be flammable, although extensive testing has failed to show this actually happening. The general consensus is that if your clothing label says not to use fabric softener, you should take the manufacturer's word for it.

What about other fabrics?

Your fabric softener's label may also warn against use on certain other fabrics. Generally speaking, because the coating softeners leave behind could alter the fabric's performance you should not use them on any fabrics that have been designed with special qualities. That includes:

Terry cloth, which may become less absorbent as the fibers are coated with non-water-soluble residue.

Technical sportswear, which may have reduced wicking ability for the same reason.

Microfiber, which relies on its many individual fibers working independently. Fabric softener residue can fill up the spaces between the individual fibers and keep them from trapping soil.

Water-repellent fabrics, which may have reduced repellency and breathability. Fabric softener residue can cause water to spread out and soak in instead of beading up and rolling off, and it can fill in the tiny pores that allow sweat to escape.

 Make your own fabric softener & dryer sheets

Fabric softener

3 cups distilled water
1½ cup white distilled vinegar
1 cup hair conditioner

» Add ⅛ to ¼ cup softener, depending on load size, to rinse cycle or fabric softener dispenser.

Dryer sheets

Soak clean washcloths (or other cloth cut into a similar size) in fabric softener and air dry. Use as you would any other dryer sheet.

Feces

How toxic: Not toxic to toxic

Mouth	**Skin**	**Eyes**	**Inhalation**
Generally not toxic but illness is possible ▼ Rinse mouth	*Not toxic* ▼ Wash affected area	*May be irritating* ▼ Irrigate	*Not expected*

What to expect

Feces are not toxic in general, but they may carry infectious microbes that can cause illness when ingested.

Symptoms occuring within a week or two of feces ingestion should be medically evaluated, whether or not they seem related.

Human feces

Feces are typically about 30% microbes, mostly dead. The balance is made up of undigested food, epithelial cells from the intestinal lining, bile and other biological waste.

The society of microbes that live in our intestines is known as our **microbiome.** Estimates of the ratio of our gut microbes to our own human cells vary, but it is at least 1:1 and probably more. That is to say, we have at least as many microbes living in our intestines as we have cells making up our bodies.

The microbes in our gut perform tasks that are essential to life and health, like breaking down food into usable nutrients. They synthesize vitamins, train our immune system, protect us from infection and, new research reveals, likely influence our emotions and mental processes.

Each of us has a unique microbiome, but microbes of all kinds are freely passed among household members. Chances are exposure to the feces of those you live with, including cats and dogs, will not introduce many germs you don't already have.

The microbiome of the colon, or large intestine, however, is different from that of the small intestine, which is located above it. Ingestion of feces may introduce into the small intestine microbes that don't normally live there. It is also possible that infectious germs that haven't been causing symptoms may become more aggressive in the presence of certain others.

The distinctive **odor** of feces comes from chemical compounds put together by bacteria as they digest food. Because of the way our brains process odors, we perceive these compounds very differently depending on how much is present.

Indole, for example, is disgusting to us in the quantities found in feces, but in much smaller amounts it has a floral odor and it is actually used in some perfumes.

Animal feces

Examples of diseases that can be transmitted by direct or indirect contact with animal feces include:

Salmonella

Poutry such as chickens, ducks and turkeys

Cattle including calves

Rodents such as mice, rats, hamsters, gerbils and guinea pigs

Rabbits

Nontraditional small pets such as hedgehogs, chinchillas and ferrets

Reptiles such as turtles, lizards and snakes

Amphibians such as frogs and salamanders

Feeder rodents and reptiles, live and frozen

E. coli

Farm animals including cattle, chickens, turkeys, sheep, and pigs

Deer

Campylobacter

Pet store puppies

Petting zoo safety

Wash hands with soap and water or use an alcohol-based hand **sanitizer** after touching farm animals or anything in the areas where they live and roam.

Don't allow children to put **thumbs** or **fingers** in their mouths when they're around animals or in an animal area.

Don't take **strollers**, **bottles**, **pacifiers**, spill-proof **cups** or **toys** into animal areas.

Keep **food** and **drinks** away from farm animals and out of animal areas.

About feces color

Feces is generally brown, due to the presence of **bilirubin** released during the breakdown of old red blood cells. Most variations in color are related to diet but some require medical evaluation.

Red

In most cases blood is not the cause of red feces, but if there is any possibility blood could be present immediate medical evaluation is essential.

Food coloring Candy, sweet drinks, gelatin desserts, cereal, frosting, snack foods, medications

Foods Beets, red peppers, tomatoes, cranberries

Green

Usually a normal variation but more commonly seen when diarrhea causes rapid transit through the intestines. Very dark green feces may look black.

Food coloring Sweet drinks, gelatin desserts, fruit snacks

Foods Spinach and other leafy vegetables

Black

Can be due to bleeding in the stomach, which requires medical attention.

Foods Licorice, chocolate sandwich cookies, grape juice

Medications Bismuth, iron supplements

White or light grey

Very pale feces may indicate a lack of bilirubin due to problems with the liver or gallbladder, and require medical evaluation.

Medication Aluminum hydroxide antacids

Fels-Naptha

How toxic: Not toxic to minimally toxic

Mouth	**Skin**	**Eyes**	**Inhalation**
Not toxic	*May be irritating with prolonged contact*	*May be irritating*	*Not expected*
▼	▼	▼	
Rinse mouth	Wash affected area	Irrigate	

What to expect

Fels-Naptha is a solid bar and significant ingestion is very unlikely. A taste might be mildly irritating to the mouth for some.

Despite its bar form, Fels-Naptha is meant for laundry and is too harsh to use as hand soap.

Common ingredients

Back in the 19th century the Fels family added naphtha,
a petroleum-derived solvent, to their laundry soap.
Despite the name the bar no longer contains naphtha.

Fels-Naptha® comes in bar form and is used to pre-treat stains before washing and as a laundry booster. For stains the fabric is wetted and the bar is rubbed on the stain. You can also grate the soap and add it to the wash. Grated Fels-Naptha is a popular ingredient in homemade laundry detergent (see page 127).

Currently the Fels-Naptha label directs consumers to its website for an ingredient list. The site lists four kinds of soap and says the bar may contain one or more of them. Soaps (p. 162) are made by alkalinizing animal or vegetable fats; if they are alkalinized with sodium hydroxide (lye) they are **sodium soaps**. The four kinds of sodium soap that may be in Fels-Naptha are named according to their source.

Sodium cocoate is derived from **coconut oil**. It is used in a wide variety of products.

Sodium palmate is derived from **palm oil**. Over the years a great deal of old-growth forest has been cleared to make way for palm cultivation and efforts are being made to ensure palm oil used in consumer products is sustainably grown. Fels-Naptha doesn't say anything about the source of its palm oil.

Sodium palm kernelate is derived from **palm kernel oil**. This is different from palm oil in that palm oil is taken from the palm fruit, while palm kernel oil is taken from the seed, or kernel, of the fruit.

Sodium tallowate is derived from **tallow**, which is animal fat from cows and sheep. It was one of the earliest sources of fat for soaps and was once used in candles as well.

Dipentene is an ambiguous name that can refer to a molecule that is the mirror image of **limonene**, which is found in citrus fruit peels, or to a mix of **terpenes**, which are hydrocarbons found in volatile oils like turpentine, that contain limonene. Fels-Naptha seems to contain the latter.

Fatty acids are components of the fats that are alkalinized to make soap. The Fels-Naptha label lists fatty acids to match the soaps it may contain. When extra fatty acids are added to soap it is called **superfatted** and is more emollient. Superfatting helps the Fels-Naptha bar glide over the fabric when you rub it on a stain.

Fragrance has been added to Fels-Naptha according to reviews on the website. Users say the smell is very strong and unpleasant. Previously the bar had little scent if any.

 Uses for Fels-Naptha

Fels-Naptha is a laundry soap and is not intended for use as a hand or body soap. It can be irritating to skin, especially with prolonged use; use reasonable precautions.

Laundry stains

Wet the area to be treated and rub the bar over it. For greasy or oily stains that have penetrated the fabric, work the soap in with a soft brush. You can also grate the soap and add it to the wash water as a laundry booster. It is recommended to put it in first to soften in the wash water before adding clothes.

Poison ivy, oak & sumac

Fels-Naptha is reputed to effectively remove the resins of these plants. Wash skin as soon after exposure as possible and add grated soap to the wash when laundering exposed clothing.

Aphid spray

Dissolve 3 tablespoons grated soap in a gallon of hot water and allow to cool. Apply once per week as needed for aphids, mealybugs and whiteflies. The spray kills soft-bodied bugs by direct contact and doesn't have any residual effect between applications. Avoid exposing beneficial insects like bees or ladybugs.

Glass cleaner

Soak soap in water until it softens into paste. Rub a thin film on glass, allow to dry and wipe off with newspaper.

Paintbrushes

Rub paintbrush on a wet bar, work through bristles and rinse well.

DIY laundry detergent

See page 127 for recipe.

Fertilizers
How toxic: Not toxic

Mouth	**Skin**	**Eyes**	**Inhalation**
Not toxic	*Not toxic*	*May be irritating*	*Not expected*
▼	▼	▼	
Rinse mouth	Wash affected area	Irrigate	

What to expect

Fertilizers for home use are generally not toxic with a typical accidental taste or ingestion.

A dog, however, might ingest enough to have vomiting and diarrhea.

Common ingredients

Fertilizers for home use, both indoor and outdoor, are of the **NPK** type, formulated to contain specific percentages of nitrogen (N), phosphorus (P) and potassium (K).

Nitrogen is an essential component of protein-forming amino acids as well as DNA, RNA and the energy-transfer molecule adenosine triphosphate (ATP). Freed from earth's interior through the shifting of tectonic plates and then vented into the atmosphere by volcanos, nitrogen makes up 78% of the air we breathe.

All the nitrogen we inhale, though, just gets exhaled right back out again because it isn't in a form we can use. It isn't in a form plants can use, either, because nitrogen atoms in the air are too tightly bound to one another to be available for any biological process.

Before it can be used as fertilizer, the nitrogen atom pairs must be split apart and combined with other elements in a process called **fixation**.

Lightning fixes some nitrogen but more of it is fixed by certain **soil-dwelling bacteria,** the only organisms on earth known to have the enzymes needed to reclaim nitrogen from decaying organic matter. Most nitrogen for commerical fertilizers is pulled from the air.

Phosphorus, formed when stars explode and believed to have arrived on earth via meteorites, is critical for photosynthesis and plant growth, as well as formation of DNA, RNA and ATP. It also is a component of the phospholipids that form cell membranes in all life forms.

Phosphorus is not found in nature as a pure element but is combined with others in compounds called **phosphates**. Phosphorus was first isolated from urine and then from bone ash, but now most is mined as phosphate rocks or reclaimed from sewage sludge.

Potassium, unlike nitrogen and phosphorus, is not incorporated into molecules or cellular structures. Instead, potassium kickstarts and shepherds critical biological processes. In animals potassium ions move in and out of cells, affecting the flow of electrical signals. In plants, potassium ions move about influencing numerous activities from the opening and closing of stomata (the pores through which plants "breathe") to creation of ATP.

Potassium is common in soil but can't be used by plants when it is bound up in minerals that are not water soluble. Those minerals are mined to obtain **potassium chloride**, which readily dissolves in water and is used in fertilizers. Potassium chloride is used as a table salt substitute for people who have to restrict their sodium intake.

Guano is experiencing a bit of a resurgence due to modern interest in "natural" products. These bat and seabird droppings, harvested primarily in Peru, were in great demand before the advent of synthetic fertilizers. Guano is useful as a compost activator and is said to have antifungal properties.

NPK composition of guano varies depending on the diet of the animal producing it, but is generally a good source of all three major nutrients. Garden centers sell bags of dried guano and small amounts can be collected from backyard bat boxes.

Fish meal is dried and ground fish and fish offal. It is made from fish that are not considered suitable for eating, as well as "by-catch," or those that are caught unintentionally when nets are cast for more desirable species.

Touted as a natural source of nitrogen, it provides very little of this essential nutrient and comes at a high cost, both financial and environmental; it's expensive to buy for the amount of nitrogen obtained, and demand for it may contribute to an overfishing crisis.

Bone meal is made mostly from the bones of slaughtered cows, but may be made from other animals as well. It provides a small amount of nitrogen but is used for its high phosphorus content. Bone meal is only effective in soil with a pH below 7, and it is recommended to test and correct soil as needed before applying it.

Blood meal is a nitrogen amendment made of dried blood from slaughtered animals, primarily cows but also others. In the garden it tends to repel herbivores like deer and rabbits, but may attract carnivores and omnivores like raccoons and possums.

Kelp is derived from seaweed, often North Atlantic *Ascophyllum nodosum*, also known as rockweed. Available as a liquid for spraying on foliage or a dried meal for soil amendment, kelp has a modest NPK composition and a smattering of micronutrients. *A. nodosum* is fast-growing but some object to its large-scale harvesting because it provides an essential habitat for numerous marine creatures.

Manure is considered a soil amendment rather than a fertilizer, although it does provide nutrients as well. Before it is used in the garden it needs to be composted to kill pathogens and weed seeds and to reduce odor, nitrogen content and water weight.

Manure may be from cattle, horses, sheep, chickens or any other vegetarian animal—excrement from meat eaters is likely to contain pathogens that will not be destroyed through composting and may cause severe illness. Never use dog or cat droppings in the garden!

Fire extinguishers (dry chemical)
How toxic: Not toxic

Mouth	**Skin**	**Eyes**	**Inhalation**
Not toxic	*Not toxic*	*May be irritating*	*May be irritating*
▼	▼	▼	▼
Rinse mouth	Wash affected area	Irrigate	Fresh air

What to expect

The powder from a dry chemical fire extinguisher is not toxic but can be irritating to the respiratory tract if inhaled.

Some powders can be vacuumed but some need to be wetted down and wiped up; see below for more.

Common ingredients

Fire extinguishers for home use are designed to be non-toxic
and appropriate for use on all kinds of fires.

Sodium bicarbonate converts to carbon dioxide, using up oxygen and smothering the fire. The breakdown of sodium bicarbonate is an **endothermic** reaction that takes in more heat than it gives out, so it absorbs some heat from the fire. The carbon dioxide dissipates too quickly to cool the fuel, though, and won't keep the fire from starting back up if other conditions allow it.

Sodium bicarbonate is used in extinguishers for B-C and D fires (see next page). Its residue is dyed blue and can be cleaned up by vacuuming, sweeping or dry wiping.

Potassium bicarbonate, produced by reacting potassium carbonate and carbon dioxide, works in the same way as sodium bicarbonate but it is a more effective fire suppressant. It is mostly used in industrial settings where its superior power is needed. Potassium bicarbonate is also used as an oral medication to maintain normal serum potassium levels.

Like sodium bicarbonate, potassium carbonate is used in extinguishers for B-C fires. Its residue is dyed blue or purple and can be cleaned up the same way.

Monoammonium phosphate (MAP) is produced by reacting ammonia with phosphoric acid. Its high nitrogen and phosphorus content makes it popular as a fertilizer and as a nutritional supplement in animal feed. It also is used as a pH modifier in a number of foods and beverages.

MAP is the suppressant of choice for A-B-C fire extinguishers. Its residue is dyed yellow and is mildly corrosive to metals. It should be cleaned up promptly with hot water and baking soda and may require some scrubbing to remove.

About home fire extinguishers

Fires are classified by the kind of **fuel** involved, and most home fire extinguishers are formulated to work on the first three types (A, B, C).

A – Ordinary combustibles such as wood, paper, cloth, trash and plastics. Water is effective on these fires.

B – Flammable liquids such as gasoline, oil and paint as well as flammable gases like propane and butane. These substances are not water-soluble and pouring water on them can spread the fire. Commercial kitchen grease fires have their own classification but fire extinguishers for home use include them in this one.

C – Live electrical equipment including appliances and motors. The danger of live electricity puts these fires in their own class; if the electricity is shut off they become A or B fires. Using water on this kind of fire creates a risk of electrical shock.

D – Combustible metals such as sodium, magnesium and potassium compounds. A car may contain some of these metals.

About fire suppressant sprays

Aerosol fire suppressants with proprietary (undisclosed) ingredients are touted as smaller, faster and more environmentally friendly alternatives to conventional fire extinguishers.

There are no safety standards for these products in the US as of yet; they cannot be sold in the state of California and Consumer Reports® has given them a rating of "Don't Buy – Performance Problems."

What the numbers mean

On a fire extinguisher label, the number before A gives you its water equivalent, with each unit of 1 equaling 1¼ gallons of water. For example, 2-A is equivalent to 2½ gallons of water.

The number before B indicates how large an area the output will cover. For example, 10-B covers 10 square feet.

There's no C number because a Class C fire is just an A or B fire with electricity.

The fire tetrahedron

The four elements every fire needs—heat, fuel, oxygen and chemical chain reaction—make up the fire tetrahedron (a pyramid with three sides and a bottom). Eliminating just one of them puts the fire out.

Fuel Combustion is a chemical process and requires a substance that can be broken apart on a molecular level to release energy. Once the fuel is expended the fire goes out.

Heat Combustion requires an input of heat energy to excite the fuel's molecules to get the process started and keep it going.

Oxygen On a molecular level combustion involves an exchange of electrons known as oxidation-reduction, and the fuel needs something to exchange electrons with. Oxygen is the most common (although not the only) oxidizer.

Chemical chain reaction Once combustion begins more energy is released than taken in. A chain reaction occurs when the heat energy released by the fire keeps the temperature high enough for combustion to continue.

Fireworks

How toxic: Not toxic to minimally toxic

Mouth	**Skin**	**Eyes**	**Inhalation**
May be irritating	*Not toxic but may cause burns*	*May be irritating*	*Not expected*
▼	▼	▼	
Rinse mouth	Wash affected area	Irrigate	

What to expect

Some chemicals used in fireworks can be toxic in sufficient quantities but accidental exposures, such as a child sucking on or biting into a single firework, should cause no more than mild irritation. The primary danger of fireworks is that they are hot and explosive by nature and can cause serious injuries when misused.

Common ingredients

Some of these chemicals can be irritating in the eyes or mouth, but
the small amounts present in consumer fireworks mean
accidental exposures are very unlikely to be toxic.

Fireworks intended for use by professionals are called **display fireworks**, and the kind you can buy for home use are **consumer fireworks**. The American Pyrotechnics Association (americanpyro.com) maintains a list of chemicals that may and may not be used in consumer fireworks.

Black powder, also called gunpowder, is the traditional explosive at the heart of aerial fireworks, the kind that launch into the air. Speciality black powders are available but the traditional mixture for fireworks is 75% potassium nitrate, 15% charcoal and 10% sulfur.

Potassium nitrate, or saltpeter, occurs naturally as a mineral called **niter** that was once mined from caves in the southern US and the Atacama Desert in Chile. It can also be extracted from urine and manure, but most potassium nitrate is now synthesized by reacting potassium chloride with nitric acid or ammonium nitrate. Potassium nitrate is 47% oxygen and is a strong **oxidizer**. Its role in black powder is to provide the oxygen needed for combustion (see page 53).

Charcoal is made by burning wood until all its easily incinerated contents are gone and it is almost entirely energy-dense **carbon**. In black powder it is the primary **fuel** for combustion.

Sulfur, the fifth most common element on earth, is a fuel but it also speeds up combustion because it burns at a lower temperature than charcoal. Sulfur was once obtained from mined compounds but most is now derived from **sour gas**, or natural gas that has a high hydrogen sulfide content.

Ironically, foul-smelling sulfur compounds are added back to odorless natural gas to make leaks noticeable.

Flash powder is an alternative explosive that burns faster, brighter and louder than black powder. Flash powder was used in 19th century studio photography; it's the stuff the photographer held up in a tray and ignited just as the picture was being taken. There are different formulations but the most common uses potassium perchlorate and aluminum powder.

Potassium perchlorate is 60% oxygen and is a very strong oxidizer. Perchlorate, an anion consisting of one chlorine atom and four oxygen atoms, occurs naturally but potassium perchlorate is manufactured.

Aluminum powder is extremely combustible and reacts violently with an oxidizer. In fact, the smaller the particle the more combustible it is, because smaller particles have so much surface area to oxidize. In 2011 aluminum dust caused explosions in two factories in China that produce casings for Apple products.

Colorants are mixed with black powder, an oxidizer and a binder and made into pellets called **stars**. Stars are packed into an aerial fireworks canister with more black powder and a fuse timed to ignite them at the proper altitude.

Red Strontium and lithium compounds

Green Barium compounds

Blue Copper compounds

Yellow Sodium compounds

Orange Calcium compounds

Glitter Antimony

Silver sparks Titanium

Sparklers

Sparklers are basically fireworks designed to burn slowly rather than exploding. They are made of a metal wire or wood stick with a coating that contains combustible **fuel** (such as iron, aluminum or magnesium), **oxidizers** that provide oxygen needed for combustion (such as nitrates, chlorates or perchlorates), a **binder** to hold it all together and keep it burning slowly (such as dextrin derived from starch or gum arabic made from the sap of the acacia tree), and optionally **colorants** such as strontium (red), copper (blue) or magnesium (white). Sparklers burn very hot (2000+ F) and touching the wire before it cools completely sizzles skin, leading to the most common fireworks-related injury.

The sparkly metal particles that combust and launch into the air are just as hot, but because they are so tiny they don't possess the energy required to transfer the heat to your skin. Sparklers made with a wood or bamboo stick instead of metal wire won't burn as hot but may be smokier and will only last for about 30 seconds. It's a good idea to have a bucket of water handy to drop sparklers into after they've finished burning. Sparklers placed on cakes will leave non-toxic but possibly unsightly metal residue on the icing.

Flea & tick treatments

How toxic: Minimally toxic

Mouth	**Skin**	**Eyes**	**Inhalation**
May be irritating	*Not toxic*	*May be irritating*	*Not expected*
▼	▼	▼	
Rinse mouth	Wash affected area	Irrigate	

What to expect

Mild oral irritation may occur with products that are not intended for ingestion.

It's not unusual to get a little spot-on product on your hands when applying; this is not toxic.

Warning
Do not mistake Advantix®, which contains permethrin, for Advantage®, which does not. Permethrin is safe for dogs but **highly toxic for cats**.

Common ingredients

The differences between insect and mammal biology means products can be both effective against fleas and ticks and safe for use in the home.

The insecticides in flea and tick products bind to specific receptors in insects' bodies and interfere with normal biological processes. Some of these receptors are also found in mammals but differences in structure and function make insect receptors a better fit.

Mammals generally clear flea and tick insecticides quickly, before they can be toxic. One important exception is **permethrin**, which is very toxic for cats because they can't metabolize it well.

Types of treatments

Spot-on

These are liquids that are applied to the back of the neck. They are not absorbed into the skin but rather pool up in oil glands that feed into hair follicles; active ingredients are continuously brought to the surface as hair grows. They spread from the neck to other parts of the body through a process called **surface translocation**.

Collars

Flea and tick collars are made of plastic or fiber with embedded insecticide(s). Some are only effective in the immediate area and some spread the active ingredient over more of the body.

Oral tablets

Short-acting tablets kills all adult fleas currently on the animal's body, while the long-acting kind continue killing for up to a month. Both require fleas to bite to be killed and so are effective only on adults.

Active ingredients

Pyrethroids

Pyrethroids are synthetic compounds based on chemicals produced by chrysanthemum flowers.

Flumethrin (collar) kills ticks but not fleas. It is used in combination with imidacloprid.

Permethrin (spot-on and collar) kills ticks and fleas. It is used in lotion form for head lice (p. 128). Although safe for other mammals, it is highly toxic to cats.

Deltamethrin (collar) has a higher potential for toxicity and is mostly used in agriculture and mosquito control in areas where malaria is endemic. It is toxic to cats.

Etofenprox (spot-on and collar) is just a little different from other pyrethroids and may be useful when resistance is an issue.

Neonicotinoids

Synthetic derivatives of nicotine, these bind to receptors in the insect's central nervous system (CNS), over-stimulating neurons until they stop functioning. They can't cross the blood–brain barrier or affect the CNS in mammals. They kill fleas but not ticks. Neonicotinoids used agriculturally may be harmful to bees.

Imidacloprid (spot-on and collar) is the oldest commercially available neonicotinoid.

Nitenpyram (oral tablet) kills adult fleas but not eggs. It enters the bloodstream quickly and kills fleas right after they bite, often before they can lay eggs.

Dinotefuran (spot-on) is a newer neonicotinoid that is considered to have a better safety profile.

Isoxazolines

These require fleas and ticks to bite and ingest blood to be affected.

Afoxolaner (oral tablet) kills fleas and ticks. It is administered once per month.

Fluralaner (spot-on and oral tablet) kills fleas and ticks. Both forms are administered once every 12 weeks.

Insect growth regulators (IGRs)

Fleas hatch as worm-like larvae that feed mostly on undigested blood excreted by adult fleas, then pass through a cocooned pupa stage before emerging as adults that need blood to lay eggs. IGRs mimic or block essential hormones, preventing fleas from successfully moving through these stages. They are usually combined with another insecticide that kills adult fleas outright.

(s)-methoprene (spot-on and collar) is a type of IGR known as a juvenile hormone analog. It prevents larvae from developing into adults.

Pyriproxyfen (spot-on) works like (s)-methoprene.

Others

Fipronil (spot-on) is a boad spectrum **phenylpyrazole**. It has a greater affinity for receptors found in insects than in mammals and binds other receptors that mammals don't have.

Tetrachlorvinphos (collar) is the only organophosphate currently in use for flea and tick control. It is considered to be of low toxicity but organophosphates are known neurotoxins and potential carcinogens.

Spinosad (oral tablet) is derived from a soil-dwelling bacterium. It is also used as a pesticide on food crops.

Floor cleaners

How toxic: Not toxic to minimally toxic

Mouth	**Skin**	**Eyes**	**Inhalation**
May be irritating	*Not toxic*	*May be irritating*	*Not expected*
▼	▼	▼	
Rinse mouth	Wash affected area	Irrigate	

What to expect

Floor cleaning products are of very low toxicity but accidental ingestions or eye splashes may be mildly irritating.

These products are not especially toxic to dogs; see next page for more.

Common ingredients

Floor cleaning products generally use the same kinds of ingredients
found in other household cleaning and personal care products.

Water is known in chemistry as the **universal solvent** because it dissolves so many other substances, and much of what ends up on your floor could be cleaned up with water alone. Floor cleaners contain small amounts of other ingredients, but like many other cleaners they are mostly water.

Surfactants are common to all kinds of cleaning products. They encourage water molecules to interact less with each other and more with whatever needs to be cleaned. They also surround oils that water can't dissolve so they can be rinsed away.

Film formers leave behind a shiny, protective coating when the water in the product evaporates. Manufacturers keep their film former recipes as trade secrets, but they may contain water-soluble cationic polymers, which are made of repeating units of identical molecules and have a positive charge. Cationic polymers are also used in hair products because they coat hair with a shiny film. Film formers may contain acrylic emulsions, the same kind of water-soluble mixture used for latex paints (which despite the name contain no latex).

Chelators bind with minerals found on dirty floors that interfere with the work surfactants do. They may also have antimicrobial properties that make them effective preservatives.

Fragrances are ubiquitous in household products but some have come under fire as potential allergens. Once protected as trade secrets, fragrance chemicals are now often listed on manufacturers' websites so people can avoid the ones they can't tolerate.

Preservatives prevent microbial contamination that would otherwise limit a product's shelf life.

Murphy® oil soap

There's no oil in Murphy oil soap, but it is derived from **pine oil**—not the essential oil distilled from twigs and needles, but the fatty oil by-product of pulping pine wood. Some swear by it but others dislike its soapy residue, which can be sticky and trap dirt.

Off-label uses include:

» Removing oil stains from fabrics

» Cleaning paint brushes and horse tack

» Washing disc brake residue off car wheels and rims

» Insecticidal spray for plants

Is Swiffer® poisonous for dogs?

Every now and then an email or social media post circulates claiming Swiffer products kill dogs. **This is a myth that has been repeatedly debunked.**

Sometimes the story says Swiffer products contain **antifreeze**, because they used to be made with a small amount of **propylene glycol (PG)**. PG is used in a vast number of consumer products because it is a solvent, humectant, emulsifier, surfactant and preservative and is **not toxic**.

PG can be substituted in antifreeze for **ethylene glycol**, which is highly toxic. Making antifreeze with PG saves lives.

 Make your own floor cleaner

Water
As needed

» Commercial floor cleaners are mostly water, and it is often all you need.

Vinegar water
1 gallon water
½ cup distilled white vinegar

» Vinegar water, like plain water, is an excellent all purpose cleaner.

Spray & mop cleaner
1 cup distilled water
½ cup distilled white vinegar
½ cup rubbing alcohol (p. 156)
2 or 3 drops liquid dish soap

» Shake well and spray.

» Wipe with a soft cloth or microfiber mop.

Do not use on stone, marble or granite.

Black tea (hardwood floors)
1 quart boiling water
2 to 4 bags black tea

» Steep tea for 10 minutes. Allow to cool.

» Dip a soft cloth or microfiber mop into the tea and wring out well; do not over-wet.

Test on an inconspicuous area to make sure the tea is not significantly darker than the wood; dilute as needed.

Fluoride toothpaste

How toxic: Not toxic to minimally toxic

Mouth	**Skin**	**Eyes**	**Inhalation**
Chronic ingestion may discolor teeth	*Not toxic*	*May be irritating*	*Not expected*
▼	▼	▼	
Rinse mouth	Wash affected area	Irrigate	

What to expect

A very large toothpaste ingestion could cause nausea and vomiting and, if it is sweetened with sorbitol, a little diarrhea.

Treatment is not needed, but you can give calcium to bind the fluoride if you wish. Calcium antacids or any form of dairy will do.

Common ingredients

The utility of fluoride was discovered in Colorado Springs. Children there had stained but decay-resistant teeth due to fluoride from Pikes Peak leaching into the local drinking water.

Sodium fluoride occurs in nature in various mineral compounds, but the fluoride for dental products is derived from **fluorspar**, a mineral form of **calcium fluoride**. It's safe to ingest in reasonable amounts and is used for fluoride tablets and fluoridated water.

Stannous fluoride gets its name from stannum, or **tin**, because it's made of fluorine bound to tin. It's more effective than sodium fluoride in preventing cavities and has the added benefit of being **antimicrobial**, which helps prevent gum disease. It's especially beneficial for people who don't make enough saliva.

Early toothpastes used stannous fluoride but it was largely replaced by sodium fluoride, which is cheaper and tastes better. After many years of being available only by prescription it is now available in a few

OTC toothpastes. It's expensive, though, can cause superficial staining of the teeth and shouldn't be used on porcelain veneers.

Sorbitol, which occurs naturally in some fruits, is derived from glucose. Studies have found that sometimes the bacteria responsible for tooth decay can use sorbitol as food, but for most people this doesn't happen or happens too slowly to be a problem.

Overall sorbitol is better for teeth than sucrose (cane or beet sugar). Large amounts of sorbitol can have a laxative effect, however, as it is hygroscopic and pulls water into the GI tract.

Saccharin was once implicated as a cause of bladder cancer in male rats, but further research found the danger was specific to rats and didn't apply to humans. Saccharin is not metabolized but is excreted from the body unchanged. It is entirely synthetic and is combined with sodium in toothpaste and food products to make it water-soluble.

Xylitol is a sugar alcohol derived from plant sources. It occurs naturally in fruits, berries, grains and trees. Xylitol not only does not promote cavities, it actually kills bacteria responsible for tooth decay. Xylitol gum and mints can be used daily to help prevent cavities, up to a maximum of about 40 grams per day; more than that may cause diarrhea. While safe for humans, xylitol is **very toxic for pets**, because in non-primates xylitol stimulates release of insulin from the pancreas and causes extreme hypoglycemia.

About the warning label

The scary warning label on fluoride toothpaste is required by the FDA because fluoride is classified as a **drug**, and all drugs must carry similar warnings. Many dental professionals object to the label's wording because it makes fluoride toothpaste sound dangerous.

While it is theoretically possible to ingest a dangerous amount of fluoride from toothpaste, this is not known to occur. The amount of fluoride in toothpaste is small and an attempted massive ingestion would be thwarted by vomiting.

How fluoride prevents cavities

Enamel, the hard white surface of teeth, is made up of densely packed mineral crystals. When we feed sugar to the bacteria in our mouth, they produce acids that dissolve the crystals in a process known as **demineralization**. Saliva neutralizes the acids and provides minerals needed to rebuild, or **remineralize**, enamel. This process occurs continuously. Tooth decay results when mineral crystals are broken down faster than they can be rebuilt.

Fluoride encourages remineralization and interferes with production of bacterial acids, but most importantly it binds with calcium and phosphorus to form crystals in the enamel that are harder than the ones they replace. (These **fluorapatite** crystals also occur naturally in sharks' teeth.) Remineralization is most effective when fluoride is applied directly to teeth, but tablets also work because the fluoride reaches teeth through saliva.

Dental fluorosis

Taking in too much sodium fluoride over a long period of time can be a problem for children up to about age eight. During the years when permanent teeth are forming, excessive hardening of the enamel can cause **discoloration** of the teeth. This won't happen with a one-time ingestion, though.

Toothpaste for sensitive teeth

The nerves inside teeth are surrounded by a porous material called **dentin**. Damage or erosion of the outer tooth can expose microscopic channels in the dentin, transmitting pain sensations to the nerves when stimulated by hot, cold, acidic or sweet foods. Toothpaste for sensitive teeth fills in the channels with **potassium nitrate** that blocks transmission of signals to the nerves.

Freon & other refrigerants

How toxic: Not toxic

Mouth	**Skin**	**Eyes**	**Inhalation**
Not toxic	*Not toxic*	*May be irritating with direct contact*	*Rarely irritating*
▼	▼	▼	▼
Rinse mouth	Wash affected area	Irrigate	Fresh air

What to expect

When you puncture your refrigerator or freezer's tubing, the gas released is only toxic in that it displaces oxygen in the air. Open doors and windows and use a fan if necessary to clear the air. No special precautions are needed when cleaning up liquid refrigerant. It isn't harmful to touch and won't poison your food.

Common ingredients

Freon® is a brand of chlorofluorocarbons that are being phased out due to their ozone-depleting properties. Although the term is commonly applied to all refrigerants, modern home appliances don't contain Freon.

Refrigeration, like air conditioning, is a **heat transfer system**. It may seem that when we put food in the refrigerator the food absorbs the cold, but actually the heat is being pulled out of the food. The refrigerant is in gas form as it flows through tubing inside the refrigerator, absorbing heat. It is then compressed into a liquid and moves through a kind of radiator on the back of the refrigerator, where the heat is discharged to the air.

The refrigerant needs to be a substance that changes states (gas to liquid, liquid to gas) at low temperatures. Early refrigerants included ammonia, chloromethane and sulfur dioxide. They worked well but were toxic and were replaced with **chlorofluorocarbons** (CFCs), some of which are sold under the brand name Freon.

By the 1970s it was becoming clear that CFCs are destructive to the ozone layer that protects us from extremely dangerous solar radiation. CFCs were replaced by **hydrochlorofluorocarbons** (HCFCs), which cause less ozone depletion than CFCs but are still damaging.

By the 1990s **hydrofluorocarbons** (HFCs) that don't affect ozone were in use, but they were later recognized as significant **greenhouse gases** and are slowly being phased out. Replacements include ammonia and the hydrocarbons propane, isobutane and substance called R-441A that is a mix of ethane, propane, butane and isobutane. These are considered **natural refrigerants** because they occur in nature unlike CFCs, HCFCs and HFCs, which are man-made.

HFCs as greenhouse gases

Naturally occurring greenhouse gases make life on earth possible; without them the heat we receive from the sun would radiate right back out into space and we would freeze. Too heavy a layer of gases, though, traps excessive amounts of heat.

Whether a gas contributes to the greenhouse effect has to do with the ability of its molecules to absorb and reflect solar radiation, and that has to do with the size and shape of the molecules and how tightly bound their atoms are.

HFCs have thousands of times the warming power of carbon dioxide, and once they reach the upper atmosphere they persist for 20 to 120 years. There is global agreement that HFCs need to be phased out but that's going to take time, first for alternatives to be developed and approved, and then for new appliances to be designed and manufactured to use them.

CFCs and ozone depletion

The oxygen we breathe is actually dioxygen, or two oxygen atoms bound together ($O2$). Ozone is made of three oxygen molecules bound together ($O3$). A layer of ozone in the upper atmosphere absorbs all deadly UV-C rays from the sun and most of the harmful UV-B rays. While $O2$ is necessary for life, it does not absorb UV rays as effectively as $O3$ and depletion of ozone allows more harmful radiation to reach the earth.

When a CFC molecule in the upper atmosphere is hit by UV rays a chlorine atom breaks away. If the chlorine atom collides with an ozone molecule, it takes one of the three oxygen atoms to form a chlorine monoxide molecule and leaves the other two as dioxygen ($O2$).

UV rays also split some $O2$ molecules into single oxygen atoms. When one of these comes across a chlorine monoxide molecule, it takes the oxygen atom and reverts to $O2$, and the chlorine atom is freed to go destroy another ozone molecule. A single chlorine atom can continue to ping around the upper atmosphere like this until it has destroyed 100,000 ozone molecules.

Preventing frost

Warm, moisture-containing air enters the freezer every time the door is opened. The moisture condenses and freezes, turning to **frost**. The best way to prevent frost build up is to limit the amount of warm air going into the freezer.

Organize the contents so you don't have to keep the door open while you search for something, and keep the freezer **fully stocked** to minimize the space available for warm air to fill. If you're low on frozen foods you can take up the empty space with crumpled newspaper or containers of water.

Self-defrosting freezers

Self-defrosting freezers have warming coils embedded in them that come on periodically long enough to melt accumulated frost but not long enough to lower the temperature in the freezer. Melted frost drains to the bottom of the freezer and evaporates.

Gasoline

How toxic: Minimally toxic to extremely toxic

Mouth	**Skin**	**Eyes**	**Inhalation**
May be irritating; taste may persist	*May be drying*	*May be irritating*	*Toxic when abused*
▼	▼	▼	▼
Rinse mouth	Wash affected area	Irrigate	See page 19

What to expect

Swallows of gasoline usually occur while siphoning and may cause a burning sensation in the throat and stomach. Many people find drinking milk soothes the throat, and antacids may help the stomach. Persistent burping with gasoline taste is common. NEVER force vomiting after gasoline ingestion as it increases irritation and risk of aspiration.

Warning

Aspiration Gasoline can enter the lungs when it is swallowed or vomited, leading to life-threatening pneumonitis. Get immediate medical care for coughing or difficulty breathing, or if aspiration cannot be ruled out.
Inhalation Intentionally inhaling gasoline fumes can cause cardiac dysrhythmias and sudden death, even in an otherwise healthy person.

Gasoline is a mixture of hundreds of petroleum-derived hydrocarbons, which are composed solely of carbon and hydrogen. Some brands of gasoline contain additives such as lubricants, detergents and corrosion inhibitors.

Petroleum products are poorly absorbed through the GI tract, presumably because they are not commonly encountered in the natural environment and so we never evolved the ability to metabolize them. This means they pass through the GI tract unchanged and while swallowing a hydrocarbon may be unpleasant, it won't cause systemic toxicity.

Some gasoline additives are inherently toxic and are regulated to limit environmental damage from vehicle exhaust and fuel spills. Many would also be toxic if ingested in sufficient quantity but it is virtually impossible to drink enough gasoline to be poisoned by its additives.

Hydrocarbon **vapors**, however, are readily absorbed through the lungs and easily cross the blood–brain barrier. Toxicity is not expected with casual exposure such as stopping at a service station for a tank of gas, but intentional inhalation (sniffing, huffing, bagging) has a wide range of neurological effects from euphoria, slurred speech and confusion to hallucinations and coma. Chronic inhalation can have lasting effects including hearing loss and memory impairment.

Intentional gasoline inhalation also has a direct effect on the heart and can lead to what is known as **sudden sniffing death syndrome** (SSDS). Inhalants sensitize the heart so that a jolt of adrenaline from being startled or threatened causes it to beat wildly and stop. Twenty-two percent of SSDS cases occur in those who are experimenting with inhalation abuse for the first time.

What is octane?

In a car engine's cylinders the gasoline is compressed, condensing a lot of energy into a small space, until the firing of a spark plug causes it to explode. More energy is released from the explosion than it takes to initiate it, and that released energy powers the engine.

Octane rating is not the percentage of octane in the gasoline; it signifies how much the gasoline can be compressed before it spontaneously combusts. When gasoline combusts before the spark plug ignites it, the result is audible engine **knocking**, which can damage the engine.

The higher the octane number, the more the gasoline can be compressed, and the more it is compressed, the more power is released when it is ignited. High-performance engines require a higher octane **premium** fuel, but a car that is designed for **regular** lower-octane gas can't make use of the extra power and won't run any better on premium.

A gas station may offer up to five grades of gas but have as few as two storage tanks, mixing fuel at the pump to obtain the desired octane level.

Diatoms, not dinosaurs

The petroleum that gasoline comes from was formed from diatoms (algae) and plants, not dinosaurs.

As microscopic sea life in ancient oceans died, it rained down on the sea floor and decomposed. Bacteria scavenged elements such as nitrogen and phosphorus, leaving behind carbon and hydrogen.

Soil, clay, minerals and the remains of other sea creatures accumulated on top of the deposits, in time creating enough pressure and heat to recombine them into compounds known as **hydrocarbons**. This process took millions of years, making petroleum a limited and non-renewable resource. One day fuel oil may be harvested from microalgae farmed for that purpose, but for now it's not economically feasible. Algae oil's high omega-3 fat content, however, makes it a popular dietary supplement.

What about ethanol?

Henry Ford believed ethanol was the fuel of the future and designed the Model T to run on ethanol, gasoline or a mixture of the two. Other vehicles including farm tractors also ran on ethanol, which burns cleanly, efficiently and without knocking.

Progress in the 1930s toward the replacement of gasoline with ethanol caught the attention of the American petroleum industry, which stepped in to put a stop to it.

The oil crises of the 1970s renewed interest in ethanol as a fuel, though, and while it hasn't replaced gasoline it is now a common gasoline additive.

Gentian violet

How toxic: Not toxic to minimally toxic

Mouth	**Skin**	**Eyes**	**Inhalation**
May be irritating	*May stain*	*May be irritating*	*Not expected*
▼	▼	▼	
Rinse mouth	Wash affected area	Irrigate	

What to expect

Gentian violet is safe for use in the mouth but too much can be irritating to mucous membranes, and a full swallow may upset the stomach.

You should not expect any significant problems, but seek medical attention if a baby is not feeding normally after exposure to gentian violet.

Gentian violet is named for its **color** and not because it is derived from gentian flowers. It is actually derived from **coal tar**, a traditional treatment for scaly skin conditions like eczema and psoriasis.

Gentian violet is considered to be a safe, effective treatment for thrush both in baby's mouth and on mom's nipples, but it is mildly corrosive and can cause sores in the mouth if overused.

Gentian violet is sold as a 1% or 2% solution in ethanol and water. It has been shown to be effective at much lower concentrations, however, and it can be made less irritating by diluting with water.

The safest way to apply gentian violet to a baby's mouth is by dabbing it on with a **cotton swab**. A swab can also be used to paint mom's nipples. It's safe to nurse the baby with the gentian violet on the nipples; in fact, this is another way to apply it to the inside of baby's mouth.

Gentian violet has also been shown to be effective against oral thrush in those with HIV, and some find its taste less objectionable than the alternative, nystatin.

Preventing gentian violet stains

Gentian violet will stain skin, clothing, bedding and anything else it touches, and the stains are persistent. It's best to try to avoid them.

» Apply vegetable oil, lanolin or petroleum jelly to baby's lips.

» Undress your baby and yourself to the waist while applying gentian violet and while nursing.

» If possible, wear older clothing that you won't mind staining.

» If not nursing immediately, allow nipples to air dry before getting dressed.

» Nursing pads will help protect clothing.

Gentian violet for hair

Use a medicine dropper when adding to water or hair products. Wipe spills on hard surfaces immediately with rubbing alcohol.

Small amounts of gentian violet applied to blonde hair cancels out **yellow tones**, making hair brighter and more platinum. Larger amounts dye hair various shades of purple, depending on how much is used.

To tone down brassiness, add just a few drops to a bottle of shampoo or conditioner and use normally. If your hair begins to take on a purple hue you don't like, use regular shampoo for a while.

To **dye** hair purple add the gentian violet to conditioner and apply to hair, allowing it to remain until you reach the shade you want. Alternatively you can just mix it with water and apply.

Removing gentian violet stains

Removing gentian violet stains from skin

Gentian violet stains on skin will fade within a day or so of discontinuing its use, but you can also wipe stains with rubbing alcohol or a pure unflavored vodka and rinse with water.

Removing gentian violet stains from fabric

You may not need every step on this list, but you will need patience whichever steps you take. Please note that you must rinse out vinegar and ammonia completely before using bleach, as we never mix them (see page 43 for more on this).

First, make a detergent solution by mixing 1 teaspoon mild **liquid hand dishwashing soap** with 1 cup water. Divide solution and add a few drops of **vinegar** to one half and a few drops of **ammonia** to the other.

1. Sponge stain with plain water.

2. With absorbent pad, apply detergent solution with vinegar to stain. Let stand 30 minutes or more, blotting every 5 minutes with a clean pad moistened with the detergent solution. Flush with water.

3. With absorbent pad, apply rubbing alcohol or pure unflavored vodka to stain. Cover the stain with the pad. Change pad as it picks up stain, pressing hard each time. Flush with alcohol. Allow to dry.

4. Sponge stain with water.

5. With absorbent pad, apply detergent solution with ammonia to stain. Let stand 30 minutes, blotting every 5 minutes with clean pad moistened with detergent solution. Flush with water and allow to dry.

6. Dilute 1 teaspoon of chlorine bleach with 1 tablespoon water. Apply bleach solution to stain with a medicine dropper. Do not use chlorine bleach on wool, silk or spandex. Do not allow bleach to remain more than two minutes. Flush with water after each bleach application.

Glass cleaners

How toxic: Not toxic to minimally toxic

Mouth	**Skin**	**Eyes**	**Inhalation**
May be irritating	*Not toxic*	*May be irritating*	*Not expected*
▼	▼	▼	
Rinse mouth	Wash affected area	Irrigate	

What to expect

Glass cleaners may be slightly irritating in the mouth or eyes, especially if they contain ammonia.

No special steps need to be taken beyond the usual advice for rinsing the mouth and irrigating the eyes.

Common ingredients

Glass cleaners are mostly water. Some of the other ingredients can be toxic, but they are present in quantities much too small to more than irritating.

Water is the primary ingredient in glass cleaners, making up as much 99% of the product.

In chemistry it is said that **like dissolves like**—that is, negatively charged solvents dissolve negatively charged substances, and positively charged solvents dissolve positively charged substances.

Water molecules are **polar**, having a slightly negative charge on one end and a slightly positive charge on the other, so it can dissolve most substances regardless of the charge. For this reason water is known as **the universal solvent**.

Water does have some limitations when it comes to cleaning glass, though, and a few other ingredients are added to make a more effective cleaner.

Alcohols are solvents that evaporate quickly, a desirable trait in a glass cleaner. **Propylene glycol butyl ether** (PGBE) and **methoxyisopropanol** (propylene glycol methyl ether, PGME) are alcohols that are also widely used in cosmetics and personal care products.

Isopropyl alcohol isn't commonly found in commercial products but is a very effective glass cleaner.

Surfactants break up water's surface tension so it spreads over the glass instead of beading, and surround oils to separate them from the glass surface.

Ammonia (p. 28) works well because it is alkaline and so saponifies, or turns to soap, oils and grease. It must be used sparingly as its vapors are strong and biting.

Microfiber cloths

Microfiber cloths are woven from plastic fibers that are so tiny they can latch onto individual bacteria and hold them, rather than just pushing them around as a larger fiber (cotton, for example) would do. Because they are plastic the microfibers also have a little bit of an electrical charge, and they attract and hold dirt and oils on a molecular level. Microfiber cloths don't require soap or much water to work; in fact, using soap interferes with their cleaning ability. A small amount of water applied to a surface does help dissolve any soil sticking to it so the cloth can wipe it away. If your window is visibly soiled you should clean it first with plain water, vinegar water or another solvent, then wipe it with a slightly moistened microfiber cloth for a shiny, streak-free clean.

What about newspaper?

Newspaper is a traditional window-cleaning tool that actually works pretty well. It's cheap, absorbent, recyclable, doesn't scratch and can be used with white vinegar or any other glass cleaning solution. Today's vegetable-based inks are less likely to rub off than the petroleum-based inks of the past, but you might still want to be careful around white trim.

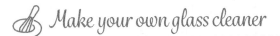

Make your own glass cleaner

Recipes for glass cleaners using various combinations of ingredients abound and each has its fans; the following should be considered a guide to help you come up with a mixture that works for you.

You can use tap or filtered water, but distilled water is best as the distillation process removes minerals that can make cleaners less effective. There's no apparent explanation for why cornstarch makes a good window cleaner but it's a popular addition.

- » 1 part white vinegar
  1 part water

- » 1 cup rubbing alcohol or vodka
  2 tablespoons white vinegar
  1 cup water

- » ¼ cup white vinegar
  1 tablespoon cornstarch
  2 cups water

- » ½ cup ammonia
  ½ cup white vinegar
  2 tablespoons cornstarch
  3 to 4 quarts water

- » ½ cup ammonia
  2 cups rubbing alcohol
  1 teaspoon liquid dish detergent (Dawn®)
  2 quarts water

Glow products

How toxic: Not toxic to minimally toxic

Mouth	**Skin**	**Eyes**	**Inhalation**
May be irritating	*Not toxic*	*May be irritating*	*Not expected*
▼	▼	▼	
Rinse mouth	Wash affected area	Irrigate	

What to expect

Oral exposure to the liquid in glow products is common. The liquid sometimes causes a mild burning sensation in the mouth, but the only treatment needed is rinsing with plain water.

Eye exposures are much less common and the liquid is not unusually irritating to eyes. The inner capsule is glass but capsule-related injuries have not been reported.

Common ingredients

All glow products, regardless of shape, size or purpose, rely on chemiluminescence, the production of light through chemical reactions.

Esters are a class of chemical compounds that make up most of the contents of a glow product. Esters are derived from reactions between acids and alcohols, and while some are produced synthetically others are part of natural biological processes.

Diphenyl oxalate is synthesized by reacting phenol, usually derived from petroleum, with oxalic acid, an organic compound that is found in many foods.

The plasticizer **dibutyl phthalate** is an ester that is common in glow products but it, along with other phthalates, is falling out of favor due to concerns chronic exposures may have endocrine-disrupting effects.

Hydrogen peroxide (p. 118) is enclosed in a glass capsule within the glow product. When the outer casing is bent the capsule ruptures, releasing the hydrogen peroxide.

The peroxide initiates breakdown of the ester, starting a series of chemical reactions that result in the release of carbon dioxide and energy.

Fluorescent dyes are generally derived from **anthracene**, which is recovered from coal tar. The dye molecules absorb the energy released by the ester breakdown and become excited, then as they relax to their normal state they emit **photons**—energy in the form of light.

The chemical structure of the dye determines how much energy it absorbs and releases; lower energy levels give off red light, while higher energy levels give off blue light.

Once all the ester has been broken down the energy transfer ends; the glow dies out and can't be restarted.

How light is produced

What we think of as light is actually **electromagnetic radiation**. Radiation that is very low in energy and moves in long, lethargic wavelengths, as well as radiation that is very high in energy and moves in short, tightly packed wavelengths, is invisible to us. The very narrow portion of the electromagnetic spectrum that we can see is called **visible light**.

Incandescence is light that is produced as a by-product of **heat**, such as from candles and incandescent light bulbs (p. 56).

Luminescence is light that is produced without heat, also known as **cold light**. There are several different kinds:

» **Chemiluminescence** is production of cold light through chemical reactions. This is how glow products work (see previous page).

» **Bioluminescence** is chemiluminescence by living organisms. Fireflies, angler fish and some kinds of bacteria, fungi and algae are bioluminescent.

electromagnetic spectrum

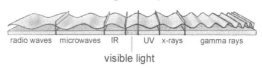

radio waves   microwaves   IR | UV x-rays   gamma rays

visible light

» **Fluorescence** is the absorption of short wavelength radiation followed by the immediate emission of longer wavelength radiation. We can't see the ultraviolet (UV) radiation given out by a black light, for example, but white objects like clothing and teeth absorb the UV light and return less energetic, longer-wavelength light that is visible to us. Once the black light is turned off the fluorescence stops.

» **Phosphorescence** is similar to fluorescence except the longer-wavelength light is emitted much more slowly, so the process continues after the external light source is removed. This is how glow-in-the-dark products work; they get charged up when exposed to bright light, then continue to emit visible light for a period of time after the light is turned off.

 *Glow stick projects*

Glow balloons

Inflate each balloon part way. Carefully insert an activated glow stick into the balloon, finish inflating and tie off.

Glow cups

Activate flexible glow sticks, bend into circles and place in the bottom of opaque plastic cups. Place clear plastic cups inside the opaque cups and press to secure. Add ice and clear liquid.

Glow jars

Prepare jars by coating with frosted spray paint and allowing to dry. Place activated glow sticks inside jars, turning them upside down if desired.

Glues & pastes
How toxic: Not toxic

Mouth	**Skin**	**Eyes**	**Inhalation**
Not toxic	*Not toxic*	*May be irritating*	*Not expected*
▼	▼	▼	
Rinse mouth	Wash affected area	Irrigate	

What to expect

Glues and pastes are not toxic when ingested although, just like anything else, they may be irritating if they get in eyes.

Super glue

Only super glue needs any kind of special treatment. See the opposite page for how to handle super glue exposures.

White glue

Once made with casein, white glue is now made with the non-toxic synthetic **polymer polyvinyl acetate** (PVA), which is suspended in water. Some brands may contain glycerin (p. 108) and silicones to keep the glue smooth and squeezable. White glue peels off easily.

Glue sticks

Glue sticks are made of polymers combined with surfactants to give them shape, and solvents to keep them from solidifying before use. Glue stick packaging was inspired by lipstick tubes. Stick glue washes off with soap and water.

Paste

Paste is **starch** suspended in water. The starch may be flour, cornstarch, potato starch or any other complex carbohydrate.

Pastes made from methylcellulose or other starches are easy to clean up or unstick because they will dissolve in water even after they have dried.

Epoxy adhesive

Polymers are molecules made up of chains of repeating units. They tend to be pretty stable. When these chains line up next to each other and form connections between them, like rungs on a ladder, they become locked in place. Epoxy adhesives for home use come in two parts: the **epoxy resin**, and a **hardener**. When they are mixed together the hardener causes links to form between the epoxy chains so they form a rigid structure. Epoxy adhesives can be removed from skin with vinegar or nail polish remover.

Super glue

These glues contain **cyanoacrylates** (CA). Exposure to water molecules—which are present in the air and on the surface of pretty much everything—starts a chain reaction in which the CA monomers rapidly bond into rigid polymers. What distinguishes CA from other glues is the speed with which they polymerize and the strength of the bonds they form.

Removing super glue from . . .

Skin Super glue on the skin is harmless but may be irritating or distressing, especially when fingers are glued to each other or to another object. Soaking in warm water is sometimes sufficient to loosen it, but it can also be massaged with vegetable oil, peanut butter or mayonnaise. Acetone nail polish remover is an excellent super glue solvent but it can be irritating and should not be used on babies or on large areas of skin.

Mouth Super glue begins to harden as soon as it comes in contact with saliva, at which point it becomes an inert **foreign body**. Swallowed bits of super glue will pass through the GI tract uneventfully. The glue may, however, adhere to teeth, tongue or cheeks. If this is not causing any irritation, just let it be; it will wear off. Otherwise, you can try brushing gently with a soft toothbrush, or rubbing with vegetable oil or peanut butter.

Eyes Super glue most commonly gets in eyes when it's mistaken for eye drops. Usually the worst that happens is the eyelids are glued shut, but the glue may harden and scratch the cornea. If this happens, cover the eye with a cloth and head to the emergency room. If eyelids are glued shut, irrigate with warm water or apply a washcloth frequently rewetted with warm water. Gently massaging the lashes with vegetable oil, mayonnaise or ophthalmic ointment may help. If there's no pain and no extenuating circumstances such as a contact lens in place or a history of cataract or lasik surgery, it's probably safe to wait to see if these measures work. Otherwise, it's a trip to the emergency room. Don't take chances with eyes—they are irreplaceable!

How does glue work?

Most of the things we want to stick together—two pieces of paper for example—won't stick by themselves; we need to sandwich between them something that will hold them together. That something needs to have two qualities: **adhesion**, or the ability to stick to other things; and **cohesion**, or the ability to stick to itself. If the glue between two pieces of paper sticks to the papers but can't stick to itself, the papers will easily pull apart, each with some of the glue on it. Natural materials that exhibit both adhesion and cohesion are found among plant starches, tree resins and animal proteins.

Some adhesion is due to differences in **electrical charge** between molecules, causing those with negative charges to adhere to those with positive charges. Some is due to **mechanical locking**, in which the glue spreads into irregularities in an object's surface and hardens in them. And some is due to **chemical reactions** in which the object being glued melts and reforms with the glue into a new compound. There are other theories of adhesion, but these cover the kinds found in household products.

Who's Elmer?

Borden milk's famous spokescow, **Elsie**, had a husband named **Elmer**. Borden also made a casein-based glue (casein is a milk protein) and Elmer was the obvious choice to represent it. Elmer's® glues are no longer made with casein nor are they sold by Borden, but Elmer still figures prominently on the product line's logo.

Glycerin suppositories

How toxic: Not toxic

Mouth	**Skin**	**Eyes**	**Inhalation**
Not toxic	*Not toxic*	*Not expected*	*Not expected*
▼	▼		
Rinse mouth	Wash affected area		

What to expect

Large ingestions of liquid glycerin can irritate the GI tract, but the small amount in a glycerin suppository is not expected to cause any problems.

Glycerin, also known as glycerol, is a naturally occurring **sugar alcohol** with chemical characteristics of both sugars and alcohols (but not the intoxicating kind).

A glycerin molecule with three fatty acids attached is known as a **triglyceride**, a common kind of fat that is found in both plant and animal tissues. Glycerin is recovered as a by-product when fats are saponified, or alkalized to make **soap** (p. 162), although it can also be synthesized from petroleum-derived **propylene**.

Glycerin is widely used in cosmetics, pharmaceuticals and food products because of its **hygroscopic**, or water attracting, qualities. It's used medically to reduce eye and intracranial pressure. In fact, it's so effective at trapping water that it is being used as a medium to extract water from the air in places where potable water is scarce (see next page for more).

Glycerin is a syrupy liquid and is mixed with other ingredients like wax and gelatin to form suppositories that are firm enough to insert but quickly melt at body temperature.

Glycerin suppositories work by drawing in water, softening stool and increasing pressure in the rectum, which in turn stimulates **peristalsis** (the wavelike muscle contractions that propel the stool).

Glycerin can be purchased in liquid form and may be taken by mouth as a laxative, but it's seldom used this way anymore because it tends to cause nausea and vomiting when ingested in quantity. The amount of glycerin in a rectal suppository is too small to cause these kind of effects when accidentally ingested.

Water from air

A Swiss humanitarian foundation called **Sanakvo** (*healthy water* in Esperanto) has developed a simple, low-tech system for extracting potable water from the air that it hopes to introduce in areas where clean water is scarce.

As shown in the schematic, fabric soaked in glycerol is hung on a clothesline where it traps atmospheric water.

The glycerol-water solution is then heated by the sun, causing the water to vaporize and pass through a porous membrane.

As the collected vapor cools it condenses back into liquid and flows into a storage vessel.

Sanakvo estimates that a line that is 60 meters (66 yards) long hung with double fabric can absorb up to 500 liters of water in 24 hours, enough to supply 200 people with a day's worth of drinking water.

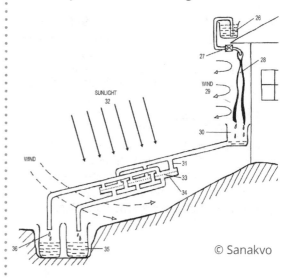

© Sanakvo

 Other uses for glycerin

Lip balm

Mix 1 part glycerin to 3 parts coconut oil.

Eyeliner (or intense eyeshadow)

Crush eyeshadow and add glycerin by the drop until desired consistency.

Facial toner

Mix ¼ cup glycerin with 1½ cup rose water. Use as a spray or apply with a cotton ball.

Moisturizing nail polish remover

5 ounces acetone
1 tablespoon glycerin
3½ teaspoons water

Add to other products

Lotions, shampoos and conditioners can be made more moisturizing by adding a small amount of glycerin. Start with a pea-size amount because adding too much will make the product sticky.

Hair dyes

How toxic: Not toxic but sensitivity reactions may occur

Mouth	Skin	Eyes	Inhalation
Not toxic	*Sensitivity reaction is possible*	*May be irritating*	*Not expected*
▼	▼	▼	
Rinse mouth	Wash affected area	Irrigate	

What to expect

Home hair coloring products are usually not toxic or only slightly irritating, but sometimes cause sensitivity reactions. These reactions usually occur when the product is used as intended, not when a small accidental exposure happens. Symptoms may appear immediately or days after the hair is colored. As with other allergic reactions, most can be treated at home but severe cases may require medical attention.

Common ingredients

Hair coloring products for home use contain the same kind of ingredients as those used in salons. They are formulated to give consistent results under ideal conditions; actual results may vary.

Dye precursors are colorless substances that undergo chemical changes during the dyeing process to form desired hair colors. Precursors are mostly **amines** and **phenols** and are too many to list here.

Hydrogen peroxide (p. 118) is the active ingredient in hair dye **developer** and has two jobs. First it oxidizes the melanin already present in the hair's cortex, breaking the molecular bonds that hold the melanin together. As the melanin comes apart **sulfur** atoms are released, giving the process its distinctive odor. The hydrogen peroxide then oxidizes the dye precursors to make them ready to bind with couplers. Developers come in different volumes that correspond to the percentage of peroxide in them. **10 volume** has 3% hydrogen peroxide and is used when color does not need to be lifted, or lightened. **20 volume** has 6% peroxide and will lift color one or two shades; it's considered the ideal volume for covering grey. **30 volume** has 9% peroxide and will lift color three or more shades. Higher volume developers are available but are not recommended for home use as they can be extremely corrosive.

Ammonia (p. 28), in the form of ammonium hydroxide, is the most common alkali used in hair dyes. Its high pH causes the **cuticle** scales to swell and separate so the dye molecules can reach the cortex. This is essential for **lifting**, or removing, some of the hair's natural color if you want to go lighter, and for effectively coloring grey hair. Ammonia can also damage the cuticle, especially with repeated use.

Ethanolamine is the most common ammonia substitute used in **ammonia-free** hair color products. It is less effective for lifting color and while it lacks ammonia's pungent odor, it is an ammonia derivative and can still damage hair.

Resorcinol, the most common dye **coupler** in **permanent** hair coloring products, occurs naturally in a number of plants and is produced commercially from benzene. After the hair's cuticle is opened, couplers and oxidized dye precursors enter the hair's cortex and combine into larger molecules, forming the desired color and becoming trapped in the cortex.

Types of hair dye

Temporary dyes coat the cuticle with pigment and wash off with one shampoo.

Semi-permanent dyes lift the cuticle scales enough to slip small molecules of pigment under them; some of this unanchored pigment will wash out with each shampoo.

Demi-permanent dyes penetrate the cortex and deposit pigment molecules that last longer than semi-permanent pigment but will gradually wash out.

Permanent color undergoes a chemical process within the cortex, forming large pigment molecules that can't slip through the cuticle and won't wash out.

 Do your own hair color

Henna

Made from dried, powdered leaves of the *Lawsonia inermis* tree, henna deposits a subtle reddish tint but can be mixed with other plant dyes for a wider range of color. Avoid **black henna**, which may contain a coal tar dye that can cause severe skin reactions.

Natural dyes

A variety of herbs, fruits, nuts and other natural substances are said to impart color to hair. Most are made into tea or paste and require several applications to achieve the desired color. Instructions and further information are readily available online.

molecules of hair dye

Cuticle

Cortex

Medulla

permanent   demi-permanent   semi-permanent

Lighter Lemon juice, honey, calendula, chamomile, vinegar

Darker Coffee, black tea, walnut shells, sage, rosemary, nettle, rhubarb root

Red Beets, carrot juice, Jamaican sorrel, calendula, marigold, rosehips, hibiscus

Various Powdered drink mix (such as Kool Aid®)

Hand sanitizers

How toxic: Minimally toxic to toxic

Mouth	**Skin**	**Eyes**	**Inhalation**
May be intoxicating	*May be drying*	*May be irritating*	*Not expected*
▼	▼	▼	
Rinse mouth	Wash affected area	Irrigate	

What to expect

Alcohol-based hand sanitizers require a very high percentage of alcohol (60% to 90%) to be effective and ingestion can cause a dangerously high blood alcohol level.

It doesn't take much alcohol to be toxic for a child; if the amount ingested is large or unknown or if the child is symptomatic, immediate medical care is needed.

Warning

A hand sanitizer that contains 60% alcohol is the equivalent of 120 proof liquor. Alcohol-based products should be kept well out of the reach of children as well as adults with cognitive deficits and anyone else who should not consume alcohol.

Common ingredients

Ideally hand sanitizers will kill pathogenic microbes while doing little damage to skin's beneficial bacteria. Sanitizers complement rather than replace hand washing.

Water is listed as an inactive ingredient in hand sanitizers but that's inaccurate. Water does much more than dilute the other ingredients, especially in alcohol-based products. Water, the universal solvent, helps alcohol bind to a microbe's outer membrane so it can get inside and destroy it. And because water evaporates more slowly than alcohol, it keeps the sanitizer solution on the skin longer, giving the alcohol more time to work.

Without added water, alcohols are believed to damage proteins on the surface of a microbe's membrane so quickly that they coagulate into a protective shell, keeping the alcohol from penetrating further. Given time the alcohol could still do some damage, but without the added water it would evaporate too soon to be effective.

Isopropyl alcohol (p. 156) and **ethanol** are the most widely used active ingredients in hand sanitizers. They need to make up at least 60% and no more than 90% of the sanitizer liquid or gel to be effective in killing germs, but the ideal concentration is considered to be 70%. Alcohols can be drying to skin and many products add aloe or various oils to minimize drying.

Alcohols don't kill spores, which are a kind of armor some bacteria retreat into under harsh conditions, and so are not used for sterilizing medical equipment except for noninvasive items like stethoscopes. As hand sanitizers alcohols have two drawbacks: They are **flammable**, and they are **intoxicating** when ingested.

Benzalkonium chloride, a type of cationic **surfactant** known as a quaternary ammonium compound, is the most common antimicrobial found in **alcohol-free** hand sanitizers. It is also used as a surfactant, biocide and preservative in pharmaceuticals and consumer products. It's less drying to skin than the alcohols and is not intoxicating when ingested. Benzalkonium chloride is present in hand sanitizer in very small amounts—around 0.1%—but contact dermatitis or other irritation sometimes occurs.

Thymol, sometimes listed as *Thymus vulgaris oil*, is an essential oil with antibacterial properties that is derived primarily from **thyme**, although it is present in other herbs as well. Essential oils don't mix well with water, so hand sanitizers that utilize them also contain plant-based solvents and surfactants to make sure the oils stay in contact with microbes long enough to kill them.

Triclosan in hand sanitizers has been banned by the FDA, which found the purported antimicrobial has not been proven safe and effective for this purpose.

✍ *Make your own hand sanitizer*

It's important to remember that while typical DIY recipes may smell nice and leave hands soft, they have not been tested for effectiveness or shelf life. In a situation where someone's health depends on clean hands, you're safer using a commercial product with FDA-sanctioned ingredients. Essential oils should always be handled with care and kept well away from pets and small children, for whom they may be toxic.

With alcohol

¼ cup isopropyl alcohol or unflavored vodka
1 tablespoon pure aloe vera gel
⅛ teaspoon antibacterial essential oil (eg, thyme, oregano, tea tree, peppermint, lavender)
1 teaspoon liquid vitamin E

Without alcohol

1 ounce pure aloe vera gel or aloe/distilled water mix
2 or 3 drops each of the following essential oils:

clove bud	eucalyptus
lemon	rosemary
cinnamon bark	

aloe vera

Helium

How toxic: Not toxic to highly toxic

Mouth	**Skin**	**Eyes**	**Inhalation**
Not ingestible	*Not expected*	*Not expected*	*Dangerous when misused* ▼ See below

What to expect

Inhaling helium from a balloon is usually (but not always) harmless and the effect on the voice is very brief.

Inhaling helium directly from the tank used to fill balloons can be deadly. See below for more information.

Warning
Never inhale helium directly from a pressurized tank. See below for more.

Helium is the second most abundant element in the known universe but is relatively rare on earth. It was first thought to be found only in the sun and so was named for the Greek sun god **Helios**.

Helium is produced by decay of radioactive minerals such as cleveite. It is found mixed in with **natural gas**, with the highest concentrations in Texas, Oklahoma and Kansas. The US government runs a helium reservoir in Amarillo, Texas.

Most helium is used for medical, scientific and industrial applications. When cooled to extremely low temperatures it turns into a liquid without freezing, making it critical for use in **MRI** machines.

Why helium changes the voice

Sound moves through helium much faster than it does through air, and filling the vocal cords with helium causes a temporary change in the voice's timbre. This comical effect only lasts for a few seconds and the voice returns to normal as the helium is replaced with air.

For the most part, inhaling helium from a balloon is harmless. However, there have been reports of people **suffocating** from inhaling large quantities of helium deeply into the lungs, as it is a simple asphyxiant that displaces oxygen.

Helium from the tank kills

NEVER inhale helium directly from a pressurized tank like the kind that is used to inflate balloons. High-pressure helium can blast the lungs with enough force to form a **gas embolism**, or bubble, in the bloodstream that can quickly travel to the brain, causing a **stroke**; to the heart, causing a **heart attack**; or to the lungs, causing a quick **death**.

Homeopathic products

How toxic: Not toxic

Mouth	**Skin**	**Eyes**	**Inhalation**
Not toxic	*Not toxic*	*May be irritating*	*Not expected*
▼	▼	▼	
Rinse mouth	Wash affected area	Irrigate	

What to expect

Homeopathic products are generally not toxic. However, some liquid products contain up to 20% alcohol, and most homeopathic tablets contain lactose.

Homeopathic teething tablets listing belladonna (deadly nightshade) as an active ingredient are no longer sold in the US due to reports of severe adverse effects.

Homeopathy is based on the idea that symptoms of illness can be relieved by application of miniscule-to-nonexistant amounts of a substance that would, in a larger quantity, cause the same symptoms. This idea that **like cures like** is not supported by science.

Homeopathic preparations are diluted in water repeatedly until the original substance is no longer present. In fact, it is purported that every time the substance is diluted it increases in power, which is physically and chemically impossible.

Homeopathic theory holds that after the original substance has been diluted to the point of no longer being present, the water is made curative by remembering the substance that was once there. There is no scientific basis for this belief.

There are no legal standards for homeopathic products, and on occasion one is sold that by mistake actually does contain an ingredient listed on the label.

In 2010 Hyland's Baby Teething Tablets were recalled when some were found to actually contain measurable amounts of belladonna (deadly nightshade), which is listed on the label as an active ingredient.

Hyland's assured parents that the teething tablets contain just 0.0000000000002 mg of belladonna alkaloids each, or "THOUSANDS OF TIMES below even the therapeutic amounts of Belladonna used in conventional anti-spasmodic medicines that doctors sometimes prescribe . . . ." (Emphasis in the original.)

In 2016 the FDA published a warning to consumers that homeopathic teething tablets and gels had been implicated in serious cases of injury to children, including seizures, muscle weakness and difficulty breathing. These products are no longer sold in the US under any brand.

Homeopathic tablets usually contain **lactose** and should probably be avoided by those with severe lactose intolerance.

Hydrocortisone cream

How toxic: Not toxic

Mouth	**Skin**	**Eyes**	**Inhalation**
Not toxic	*Not toxic*	*May be irritating*	*Not expected*
▼	▼	▼	
Rinse mouth	Wash affected area	Irrigate	

What to expect

If you accidently start brushing your teeth with hydrocortisone cream, just rinse out your mouth and brush with toothpaste.

Hydrocortisone creams are pretty flavorless and any significant ingestion is highly unlikely.

Hydrocortisone is a synthetic form of **cortisol**, a steroid produced in the human body by the adrenal glands, which sit on top of the kidneys (ad+renal). Cortisol is often known as the **stress hormone** because of its role in stress response.

Cortisol is also an **anti-inflammatory**, and its synthetic form is used to treat a number of medical conditions. It's used internally in medical settings but only externally in consumer products. Over the counter products contain 1% hydrocortisone in a cream base; stronger concentrations may be prescribed for severe skin conditions.

Steroids, hormones and steroid hormones

Lipids are basically substances, like fats and waxes, that won't dissolve in water. **Steroids** are lipids that have at their core a specific arrangement of carbon atoms (three 6-carbon rings and one 5-carbon ring). The kind and number of atoms attached to that core of carbon rings makes one steroid different from another.

A **hormone** is a substance that is secreted by a gland and travels through the bloodstream to another part of the body and makes something happen there.

The pituitary gland, for example, is located deep inside the brain but fires off hormones that regulate growth, reproduction, water balance and many other processes elsewhere in the body.

A hormone can only work on cells that have **receptors**, or attachment places, for that hormone. Some hormones serve very specific purposes and only certain cells will have receptors for them, but almost every cell in our bodies has receptors for cortisol.

Steroid hormones like cortisol are, of course, both steroids and hormones. All variations on cholesterol, they are produced by the adrenal glands, the ovaries and testes and, during pregnancy, the placenta.

cortisol (n.)

"hydrocortisone," 1953; from cortisone + -ol. Chosen as a shorter and clearer alternative to hydrocortisone.

cortisone (n.)

"steroid hormone found in the adrenal cortex," manufactured synthetically as an anti-inflammatory, 1949, coined by its discoverer, Dr. Edward C. Kendall, from a shortening of its chemical name, 17-hydroxy-11 dehydrocorticosterone, which is ultimately from Latin *corticis* (genitive of *cortex*) and so called because it was obtained from the "external covering" of adrenal glands. Originally called Compound E (1936).

– Online Etymology Dictionary

Hydrogen peroxide

How toxic: Not toxic to highly toxic (see warning below)

Mouth	**Skin**	**Eyes**	**Inhalation**
Not toxic in low concentrations	*Not toxic in low concentrations*	*May be irritating*	*Not expected*
▼	▼	▼	
Drink plain water	Wash affected area	Irrigate	

What to expect

Accidental ingestion of 3% hydrogen peroxide is surprisingly common.

It isn't harmful but may irritate the stomach. Dilute it with a glass of plain water.

Warning

Highly concentrated **food grade** hydrogen peroxide is extremely corrosive and can cause fatal gas emboli with a single swallow or if poured into an open wound. This industrial product has no place in the home.

Hydrogen peroxide's chemical formula is H_2O_2 and it is sometimes thought of as "water with an extra oxygen atom." It's synthesized by capturing hydrogen from a hydrocarbon (p. 98) and bonding it to oxygen. Hydrogen peroxide is unstable and readily dissociates into water and oxygen; it's sold in dark brown bottles because exposure to light will cause it to break down. It will also decay over time, so check the label for the expiration date and discard it 6 months after opening.

The product in the brown bottle is 3% hydrogen peroxide diluted in water and is the only concentration you should have at home. It may cause mild vomiting when ingested and is used by veterinarians for this purpose. More concentrated formulations are extremely dangerous and can't be used without diluting them (see next page for more).

Hydrogen peroxide as a source of oxygen

Because oxygen is critical to life, some claim ingesting substances with "extra oxygen"—like hydrogen peroxide—will enhance health. However, we have evolved a very efficient system for providing our bodies with oxygen: We breathe it into our lungs, where it's picked up by hemoglobin in red blood cells. Our heart works as a pump to push the oxygen-carrying blood to our organs, where the oxygen is released by the hemoglobin to diffuse into cells. You can't bypass this well-adapted system and deliver oxygen directly to your cells by ingesting it.

In fact, the extra oxygen released as hydrogen peroxide breaks down in the stomach—just like the extra oxygen from an undesirable medical condition called **aerophagia**, or swallowing air—is expelled from the GI tract by burping and flatulence. It may also leave the stomach more promptly, as the rapid release of oxygen may irritate the stomach enough to cause vomiting. Highly concentrated peroxide releases such massive amounts of oxygen it may force bubbles (emboli) into the bloodstream, damaging vital organs and possibly bringing about a quick death.

Another claim sometimes made is that our immune system utilizes hydrogen peroxide and so it must be good for treating medical conditions, including cancer. It's true hydrogen peroxide is produced in our bodies, both as a toxic metabolic waste product known as a **reactive oxygen species**, and as an active agent for various purposes such as calling immune cells to a wound, but hydrogen peroxide leaves the stomach as water and oxygen, not as H2O2. Even if did remain intact, it would not be able to find its way to some specific ongoing biological process to lend a helping hand.

Hydrogen peroxide for first aid

Hydrogen peroxide kills both bacteria and healthy skin cells by pulling electrons from their cell walls, causing them to come apart. Evidence of its ability to do this well is inconclusive, though, as aerobic bacteria, like our own cells, have evolved the ability to survive oxygen's corrosive effects.

Even if household hydrogen peroxide doesn't kill microbes there is evidence that its bubble action, which is due to oxygen being released as the peroxide breaks down, helps clean debris from a wound. That doesn't make it a replacement for soap and water, though, which is still the first aid gold standard.

Concentrated (food grade) hydrogen peroxide

Whereas a 16 ounce bottle of 3% hydrogen peroxide can be purchased from any grocery or drugstore for a dollar or two, a 16 ounce bottle of 35% peroxide must be purchased from a specialty shop and will cost upwards of $20. Those who recommend taking peroxide internally admit the 35% formulation is highly corrosive and cannot be used in that concentration, and instructions are given for diluting with water to a 3% solution. Two atoms of hydrogen bound with two atoms of oxygen makes the same molecule of H2O2 no matter how it is produced or packaged, and claims that any hydrogen peroxide formulation is superior to another are unfounded.

On the other hand, exposure to concentrated peroxide by any route can be extremely dangerous. Our cells, like the cells of almost every living thing, contain an enzyme called **catalase** that quickly breaks hydrogen peroxide down into water and oxygen; peroxide bubbles in a wound because of the catalase released by damaged cells. When highly concentrated peroxide comes into contact with catalase, large amounts of oxygen are released very quickly. In a confined space, like a stomach or deep wound, so much pressure can build up that gas bubbles called **emboli** are forced into the bloodstream and travel to the heart, lungs or brain, causing catastrophic injury.

While exposure to 3% hydrogen peroxide is generally harmless, exposure to highly a concentrated form can be fatal and must be treated as a medical emergency.

Ice packs & heat packs

How toxic: Not toxic to minimally toxic

Mouth	**Skin**	**Eyes**	**Inhalation**
Symptoms possible; more below	*Not toxic*	*May be irritating*	*Not expected*
▼	▼	▼	
Rinse mouth	Wash affected area	Irrigate	

What to expect

Ammonium nitrate ingestion may cause GI upset and in rare cases methemoglobinemia (see page 170); neither is likely with an accidental taste but medical consultation would be prudent should symptoms occur. Other common ingredients are benign and many are also used in pharmaceuticals, cosmetics and food products.

Common ingredients

Most of the ingredients in ice and heat packs are common to a great many other consumer products. Because the packs are intended for contact with skin and food they are designed to be sturdy and to be non-toxic should there be a puncture or leak.

Single-use ice packs

Ammonium nitrate and **water** are the most common ingredients in single-use ice packs. Squeezing the pack releases the water and the ammonium nitrate begins to dissolve. Breaking the ammonium nitrate molecules apart is an **endothermic** process that consumes heat energy. As the water loses energy in this process its temperature drops and the pack feels cold. Over time the ammonium and nitrate particles bond with the water molecules in a process that releases heat, and the solution returns to room temperature.

Urea also contains nitrogen and is used in some products instead of ammonium nitrate. Urea is a byproduct of protein metabolism but is produced commercially by reacting ammonia and carbon dioxide.

Reusable ice packs

Propylene glycol is used for the kind of ice packs you store in your freezer and reuse. It has a very low freezing point and so it gets very cold without solidifying. It is also used as a non-toxic alternative to ethylene glycol in antifreeze (p. 34).

Hydroxyethyl cellulose is derived from cellulose, a vital structural component of plant cell walls. It dissolves in water without clumping and is used as a thickening and gelling agent in a number of products, including some reusable ice packs.

Silica gel (p. 158) is used as a thickener in some reusable ice packs, but in these products the silica gel has been coated with vinyl so it adds shape to the gel without drying it out.

Single-use heat packs

Magnesium sulfate (Epsom salt, p. 77) and **calcium chloride** are used in instant heat packs in the same way ammonium nitrate is used in instant cold packs. The difference is that the dissolution of these compounds in water is an **exothermic** reaction where more heat energy is released than taken in.

Reusable heat packs

Sodium acetate, made by reacting acetic acid (vinegar) with a sodium-containing compound such as sodium bicarbonate, is the primary ingredient in reusable instant heat packs. It's used as a pH regulator, preservative and flavoring in a number of food products including salt and vinegar potato chips.

Hand warmers

Iron powder begins reacting with oxygen in the air once the airtight plastic wrapper is removed. The rapid oxidation to iron oxide—**rust**—is an exothermic reaction.

Activated charcoal in the packet serves two purposes: It holds water that is needed for oxidation, and it spreads the generated heat throughout the mixture.

Sodium chloride (table salt) serves as a catalyst for the oxidation process (which is why driving on icy roads that have been salted with sodium chloride causes the underside of cars to rust).

Vermiculite is a **phyllosilicate** mineral, meaning its molecules are stacked up in flat layers, like phyllo dough (*phyllo* comes from the Greek word for leaf). An excellent insulator, it helps regulate the hand warmer's temperature.

How reusable heat packs work

Sodium acetate has a freezing point of 130 F and is usually solid at room temperature, yet in reusable instant heat packs it's still liquid. This is possible because sodium acetate can be **supercooled**, or made to stay liquid far below its freezing point.

You can witness supercooling first hand by placing an unopened plastic bottle of **distilled water** in the freezer and leaving it there without opening the door for 2½ hours. If all goes well (and the freezer's compressor doesn't come on and jiggle the contents), when you carefully remove it you will see it is still liquid. If you then smack it against the freezer door, though, you can watch ice crystals start forming at the site of impact and rapidly spreading through the rest of the bottle.

When you disturb the water, you create a **nucleation site**—a starting point for the formation of ice crystals. Impurities in the water can also serve as nucleation sites, which is why this only works with pure, distilled water in an unopened container.

The sodium acetate in heat packs has been supercooled and sealed in a bag with no available nucleation sites. But clicking the piece of **metal** inside the bag creates a disturbance that starts the crystallization process. As with the distilled water, you can watch the crystals spreading through the solution. And as the sodium acetate molecules snap into place, heat is released.

Once all the molecules have crystallized the solution will stop giving off heat. You can then return the crystallized solution to its liquid state by heating it to 130 F or higher, and it will be ready to use again.

Jalapeno peppers & other capsicums

How toxic: Not toxic to minimally toxic

Mouth	**Skin**	**Eyes**	**Inhalation**
May be irritating	*May be irritating*	*May be irritating*	*May be irritating*
▼	▼	▼	▼
Rinse mouth; See below	Wash affected area; See below	Irrigate	Saline rinse, steam

What to expect

Individual tolerance of ingested peppers is highly variable. Skin and mucous membranes tend to maintain a normal appearance even when the burning sensation is intense.

Water does not relieve the capsaicin-related burning sensation in the mouth and can make it worse. Dairy products should be used instead.

Jalapeno peppers (and other hot peppers) belong to the sprawling genus **capsicum**, which is in turn a branch of the *Solanaceae* family that also includes potatoes and tomatoes. Like other fruits, brightly colored peppers attract birds to eat them and excrete their seeds far and wide. Mammals serve this purpose less effectively, though, and most capsicums discourage mammalian predation by encasing their seeds in a chemical called **capsaicin**.

This works because birds lack the TRPV1 receptors that are found all over mammals' bodies. TRPV1 receptors serve a variety of purposes, but one is to alert the brain to the presence of potentially injurious heat. Capsaicin molecules happen to have the right shape to fit TRPV1 receptors, so when you bite into a hot pepper your mouth tells your brain it's on fire, and your brain responds by telling your mouth that fire hurts. It may also release endorphins to mitigate the pain, though, and make you feel a little better.

Capsaicin molecules are not water soluble and can't be dislodged from TRPV1 receptors with water; in fact, **chasing hot peppers with water likely will spread the capsaicin and activate more receptors**. The exception: Copious irrigation with water is the only effective home treatment for capsaicin in the eyes.

Help for capsaicin exposures

While no treatment has been proven to be any more effective than any other for reducing the pain of capsaicin exposure, here's some that may help.

Degreasing hand dishwashing detergent

Capsaicin is oily, so washing with a degreasing hand dishwashing soap (Dawn® is frequently recommended) helps dissolve it. Use with running water.

Baby shampoo

Often recommended for use on the face and especially around the eyes.

Dairy

Casein acts as a detergent to separate capsaicin molecules from receptors; dairy products like yogurt or sour cream that are high in casein and fat work best.

Liquid antacid

How a liquid magnesium-aluminum antacid (eg, Maalox®) reduces pain from capsaicin isn't understood, but studies have shown it does have an effect. Swish and spit for mouth exposure or apply directly to skin.

Vinegar

The acidity of vinegar is said to neutralize the alkaline capsaicin. Vinegar water can be used as a soak or a compress. You can also try sucking on a lemon or lime slice, or swishing and spitting lemon or lime juice.

Vegetable oil or peanut butter

Like dissolves like; peanut butter or any kind of vegetable oil can be rubbed into the skin or applied to the mouth to break up the capsaicin oil.

The Scoville scale

The heat of peppers has traditionally been measured in **Scoville heat units** (SHU), a scale created by pharmacologist Wilbur L. Scoville in 1912.

Scoville created his scale by diluting a pepper extract in sugar water until people tasting it could no longer detect heat. A mild pepper would require little dilution to become undetectable, whereas a very hot one would have to be highly diluted.

Nowadays the American Spice Trade Association (ASTA) uses the more scientific **high performance liquid chromatography** (HPLC) method to analyze pepper heat and report values in **ASTA pungency units**. One pungency unit equals about 15 SHU.

In 2017 a British farmer produced a pepper he calls **Dragon's Breath**, with a range topping out at nearly **2.5 million SHU**, a new world record. It displaces the **Carolina Reaper**, the previous record holder with a range of **1.6 million to 2.2 million SHU**.

The Dragon's Breath's creator believes it is too hot to be consumed and suggests that, given its numbing qualities, it might serve as an anesthetic in places where standard medical anesthetics are not available.

Peppers on the Scoville scale

Rating peppers is an inexact science even with HPLC, as capsaicin content can vary widely even among like peppers.

There's no official Scoville scale and the following estimated values are offered for comparison purposes only.

Pure capsaicin	16,000,000
Dragon's Breath	up to 2,480,000
Carolina Reaper	1,600,000–2,200,000
Habanero	100,000–350,000
Scotch bonnet	100,000–325,000
Cayenne	30,000–50,000
Serrano	6000–23,000
Jalapeno	2500–8000
Poblano	1000–2000
Pepperoncini	100–500
Bell	0

Lanolin

How toxic: Not toxic

Mouth	**Skin**	**Eyes**	**Inhalation**
Not toxic	*Not toxic*	*May be irritating*	*Not expected*
▼	▼	▼	
Rinse mouth	Wash affected area	Irrigate	

What to expect

You should not expect any problems from a taste of lanolin.

A larger ingestion could have a mild laxative effect, similar to other oils.

Lanolin, also known as **wool grease**, is a **wax** secreted by the sebaceous glands of sheep to help condition and protect their skin and wool. After shearing, the lanolin is washed out of the wool and processed for a variety of uses; about 250 ml to 300 ml is obtained from each sheep. Lanolin that is used for personal care products is highly refined to remove impurities.

Lanolin closely resembles the oils our own skin produces and is more effective at soothing and softening dry skin than petroleum products, which coat but do not moisturize. Lanolin can be made into **pharmaceutical creams** that penetrate skin well enough to work as carriers for the active ingredients, while still allowing air and water to pass through to and from the skin.

Breastfeeding mom are sometimes advised to apply lanolin to **sore nipples**; it is usually recommended to rinse before nursing but it won't hurt your baby if you forget. Products with petroleum-based ingredients form a more effective barrier against moisture and may be preferred in the diaper area.

Lanolin creams and ointments may be 100% lanolin or may be about 50% lanolin combined with other ingredients such as **beeswax**, **mineral oil** (p. 38) or **petroleum jelly** (p. 152). All of these products are equally non-toxic in small amounts and all can cause loose stools in large ingestions.

 *Make your own hand cream*

Adapted from Open University © 2006

3 tablespoons lanolin
3 tablespoons distilled water
3 tablespoons grated beeswax
½ cup almond oil
3 tablespoons witch hazel
⅛ teaspoon borax powder

Mix the beeswax, lanolin and almond oil in a glass or metal bowl. Partially fill a pot with water and bring to a boil. Rest bowl on pot and heat until the beeswax and lanolin have melted.

In another pot mix together the witch hazel, borax powder and distilled water. Heat until just boiling and then slowly pour into the melted beeswax/lanolin/almond oil mixture, stirring thoroughly. Allow to cool.

lanolin(n.)

fatty matter extracted from sheep's wool, 1885, from German *Lanolin*, coined by German physician Mathias Eugenius Oscar Liebreich (1838-1908) from Latin *lana* "wool" (from PIE root *wele- "wool;") + *oleum* "oil, fat" + chemical suffix -in.

– Online Etymology Dictionary

Laundry detergents

How toxic: Minimally toxic to toxic

Mouth	**Skin**	**Eyes**	**Inhalation**
May upset stomach; See warning below ▼ Rinse mouth	*Not toxic* ▼ Wash affected area	*May be irritating* ▼ Irrigate	*Not expected*

What to expect

A swallow of liquid detergent may upset the stomach. Powders are hard to swallow and are more likely to irritate the mouth and throat. Symptoms should be mild and resolve quickly.

Laundry pods

Vomiting, coughing, drooling or changes in breathing or alertness after laundry pod ingestion require immediate medical care. See below for more information.

Warning

Ingestion of laundry detergent single dose units—pods—can be hazardous to children and adults with cognitive deficits. Keep them well out of reach and seek medical care for anyone who has symptoms after biting into one.

Common ingredients

Surface active agents—surfactants—are the primary ingredient of laundry detergents, but a variety of other ingredients are added that are specific to fabric care.

Detergents were born of necessity during World War I, when fats for soap making were scarce. Used mostly for washing dishes and clothing, synthetic detergents don't leave soap scum on surfaces.

Surfactants have a hydrophilic end that is attracted to water and a hydrophobic end that is repelled by it. They interrupt the bonds that hold water molecules together, reducing surface tension and allowing the water to better penetrate clothing fibers. Surfactants also envelop oil deposits, isolating them from fibers and suspending them in water so they can be rinsed away.

Detergents made for **HE**, or high efficiency, washers contain low-suds surfactants. The low volume of water in an HE machine would be overwhelmed by the sudsing of a regular detergent. HE detergents can be used in conventional washers.

Builders interact with minerals like calcium and magnesium that are common in hard water. These minerals bind to surfactants and keep them from working on soil. Builders like **sodium citrate** and **complex phosphates** chelate minerals and keep them in the wash water. **Sodium silicate** and **sodium carbonate** cause minerals to precipitate, or fall out of solution. Zeolites like **sodium aluminosilicate** exchange ions, taking calcium or magnesium out of the wash water and replacing them with sodium.

Alkalis increase the number of negatively charged ions. Soil and fabric fibers are generally also negatively charged, so adding negative ions increases the repellent forces between them.

Anti-redeposition agents have negative charges and attach to fibers to repel soil. The most common agent is **carboxymethyl cellulose**, which is also widely used as a thickener and emulsifier in cosmetics, pharmaceuticals and various food products. It's most effective on cotton and cotton-blend fabrics, but polymer agents have been formulated to work better on synthetics.

Optical brighteners are colorless dyes that absorb invisible (to humans) ultraviolet light and emit visible blue light, making white fabric look whiter. No fabric is snow white by nature; it must be bleached and treated with optical brighteners to make it appear so. Repeated laundering washes brighteners away and fabric begins to revert to its original yellow or grey color. You can still buy **laundry bluing**, which contains ferric ferrocyanide, a pigment also known as Prussian blue, but modern detergents mostly employ derivatives of the hydrocarbon **stilbene**.

Enzymes are small proteins added to laundry products to break down specific soils such as proteins, starches, fats or vegetable matter. Some enzymes trim up tattered cotton fibers, releasing soil hanging on to them and leaving them smoother.

✍ Make your own laundry detergent

There are many recipes but these are typical. Washing soda acts as both an alkali and a builder, and borax does both and is also an anti-redeposition agent.

Liquid detergent

1 bar of gentle soap
  OR ⅓ bar Fels-Naptha (p. 82), grated
½ cup washing soda (p. 178)
½ cup borax (p. 46)

» Melt the soap in 4 cups water.

» Fill a five-gallon bucket half full with hot water, add the soap, borax and washing soda and mix well. Allow to sit for 24 hours.

Use 1 cup for conventional top loading washers, ½ cup for HE front loaders.

Powdered detergent

1 bar soap, grated
1 cup washing soda
1 cup borax

» Mix well, running through a food processor if desired.

Use 1 tablespoon for small loads, 2 to 3 tablespoons for larger loads.

Lice treatments

How toxic: Not toxic to minimally toxic

Mouth	**Skin**	**Eyes**	**Inhalation**
Not toxic	*May cause itching and irritation*	*May be irritating*	*Not expected*
▼	▼	▼	
Rinse mouth	Discontinue use	Irrigate	

What to expect

Accidental exposures to over-the-counter lice products are not expected to cause significant problems although sensitivity reactions sometimes occur.

Some last-resort prescription products have a greater potential for toxicity, which should be thoroughly explained by your health care provider or pharmacist.

Common ingredients

Over the counter lice products are of very low toxicity for humans, but lice have become resistant to them. Last-resort prescription treatments can be quite toxic and also may become less effective over time. Although time-consuming, removing lice eggs by hand may be the most effective, and certainly the least toxic, way to win the war on lice.

Over-the-counter treatments

Pyrethrins, of which **permethrin** is one, occur naturally in chrysanthemums, and they have been used as insecticides and bug repellents for thousands of years. Synthetic pyrethrins are also known as **pyrethroids**.

Pyrethrins attack insects' nervous systems by interfering with movement of sodium and potassium through cell walls. Pyrethrins as a rule are **non-toxic** or of very low toxicity for mammals because of our large body size and the efficient way we metabolize them. Some people may experience **allergic reactions** to naturally occurring pyrethrins, especially if they are allergic to ragweed; they don't have this problem with synthetic pyrethrins.

Piperonyl butoxide is not an insecticide, but rather is a synergist that makes insecticides more effective. It works by blocking enzymes that would break down the product's active ingredients.

Dimethicone is a silicone oil used in a number of consumer products including shampoo, food, cosmetics, caulk and other sealants as well as the classic toy known as Silly Putty®. Dimethicone blocks the lice's **spiracles**, which are the tiny openings through which they breathe. It was once thought this suffocated the lice, but now it's believed it keeps them from being able to excrete excess water. Because dimethicone's action is physical rather than chemical it's unlikely lice will develop resistance to it.

Prescription treatments

Benzyl alcohol occurs naturally in some fruits and essential oils and can also be synthesized. Benzyl alcohol keeps respiratory spiracles from closing, allowing mineral oil in the product to fill the spiracles and suffocate the lice. It doesn't kill eggs and requires two treatments a week apart. Some people have allergic reactions to it.

Ivermectin is used internally for intestinal parasites and topically for lice. It causes paralysis in lice by preventing transmission of nerve impulses. Humans have receptors for ivermectin but they are safely tucked away behind the blood–brain barrier.

Spinosad is derived from bacteria originally found growing on sugar cane. It attacks insects' nervous systems in a way that is different from other pesticides and is safe for mammals and the environment. It's used to protect stored grains and is permitted in organic agriculture. Oral spinosad products are available for controlling fleas on cats and dogs (p. 91).

Malathion, an organophosphate, paralyzes lice but is of very low toxicity to humans because we metabolize it so quickly. It also kills some louse eggs. The malathion product currently on the market is formulated with **isopropyl alcohol**, which makes it highly flammable. It is applied to dry hair and left on for 8 to 12 hours.

Lindane is a neurotoxic **organichlorine** and is a treatment of last resort. In the unlikely event you are ever prescribed this product you must follow all instructions to the letter.

 The one lice treatment that really works

You will need:

Metal nit comb & regular comb	Tissues
Hair clips	Bowl of water with a little dish soap
Vegetable oil or hair conditioner	Bath towel

» Seat child under a good light so you are at eye level with her head. Drape the towel over her shoulders. Coat her hair with vegetable oil or hair conditioner.

» Use the regular comb and clips to separate hair into small sections.

» For each section, start the nit comb at the scalp and pull all the way to the end of the hair.

» Comb each section of hair at least twice, especially around the ears and at the nape of the neck where eggs are most likely to be laid. After each pass dip the comb in the soapy water and wipe on a tissue. Repeat combing as necessary.

» Flush soapy water and tissues down the toilet.

» Shampoo the hair a couple of times if you used vegetable oil, or rinse well if you used conditioner. When the hair is dry take another good look. Slide any leftover nits down to the end of the hair and toss in the toilet; if they are stuck use scissors to snip off the hair.

» Repeat this entire process every few days for at least a month, or until you are absolutely sure there is not one remaining louse or nit.

Magnets

How toxic: Not toxic but ingestion of more than one may cause problems

Mouth	**Skin**	**Eyes**	**Inhalation**
Not toxic but see warning below ▼ Rinse mouth	*Not toxic*	*Not expected*	*Not expected*

What to expect

A single swallowed magnet may present a choking hazard, but once in the stomach it should pass through the GI tract uneventfully.

Ingestion of multiple magnets

Some magnet sets contain strong magnets that can cause internal injury if more than one is swallowed. See below for more.

Warning
Ingestion of more than one magnet requires medical evaluation and follow up even if there are no apparent symptoms.

Magnets in general are no more toxic that other foreign bodies. However, some magnet sets contain high-powered **small rare earth magnets (SREMs)** that, after being swallowed, can find each other even if they are in different locations within the intestines. When they stick together with intestinal tissue between them, they can tear a hole through the tissue or choke it off until it dies, leading to serious and even life-threatening injuries. Surgery is required to remove the magnets and repair the damage.

The **US Consumer Product Safety Commission** (CPSC) has been trying for years to remove SREMs from the market—or at least limit the strength of the kind that are small enough to be swallowed—because of the risk of injury. There's been pushback from at least one magnet company and as of this writing SREMs are still widely available.

If you choose to have SREM sets in your home keep in mind that although the greatest danger is with small children swallowing them, older kids and teens may do so as well. Their ingestions are usually accidental, occurring when they use pairs of magnets to make it look like they have facial piercings.

Rare earth magnets

Most magnets are made with easily-magnetized iron compounds. These compounds stay magnetic for a long time but there's a limit to how strong they can be made.

Very strong magnets are made from **rare earth metals**, now more properly known as **lanthanides** or **lanthanoids** (because they follow lanthanum, the first element in the group). Once thought to be rare, lanthanides are actually pretty common; it's just that they all occur together in one mineral compound and are difficult to separate from one another.

Lanthanides can be compounded with other elements to form very strong magnets. **Neodymium**, alloyed with **iron** and **boron**, is the lanthanide most commonly used for rare earth magnets.

Cow magnets

Cows don't pick through grass as they graze; whatever their lips pull up, they swallow. On farms and ranches that can include nails, staples and bits of wire.

Metal debris collects in the **reticulum**, the first of the cow's four stomachs. As the reticulum contracts to move food farther along, metal bits can push through the reticulum walls and migrate to other organs, causing a condition called **hardware disease**.

To prevent hardware disease, a cow can be fed a long, smooth magnet about the size and shape of a finger. The magnet is placed with a **bolus gun**, which is a long metal or plastic tube that bypasses the cow's swallowing mechanism and places objects (like pills and magnets) into the reticulum. The magnet settles there and collects any metal bits the cow swallows, keeping them from causing trouble.

Once placed the magnet remains in the reticulum for the rest of the cow's life. The presence of a magnet can be confirmed by holding a **compass** next to the cow in the vicinity of the reticulum.

What are magnets?

All matter is made up of atoms, which in turn have nuclei surrounded by negatively charged particles called electrons. Just as the earth rotates on its axis as it orbits the sun, an electron spins on its axis as it orbits the atom's nucleus, creating a small magnetic field.

Most substances are not very magnetic because within their constituent atoms, each electron is paired with another electron that rotates in the opposite direction and they cancel each other out. However, a **ferromagnetic** substance like iron can be treated to align its electrons, so they spin in the same direction and create a stronger magnetic field.

This kind of magnet is called **permanent**, but the electron alignment is unnatural and the magnet will lose its power over time as the electrons revert to their normal state. The only naturally occurring magnet is **lodestone**, a form of the mineral magnetite believed to be magnetized when it is struck by lightning.

Most household magnets like the ones we use to stick paper to refrigerators and calendars are made with ferromagnetic powders. They are either molded into hard shapes or mixed with polymers to make magnets that are flexible.

In magnetic construction sets designed for children, the magnets are embedded in the plastic bars or tiles; the silver balls that go between plastic bars are made of steel. Magnetic sculpture toys have steel shapes on top of a magnetic base. **Wooly Willy** toys have a magnetized stylus that moves iron filings under a plastic cover.

Modeling clays

How toxic: Not toxic

Mouth	**Skin**	**Eyes**	**Inhalation**
Not toxic	*Not toxic*	*Not expected*	*Not expected*
▼	▼		
Rinse mouth	Wash affected area		

What to expect

Modeling clays are generally made of inert materials that could present a choking hazard but are not absorbed when swallowed. Some contain wheat flour and could be of concern for celiacs. Intestinal obstruction is unlikely but medical attention would be needed for symptoms such as vomiting, constipation, loss of appetite or abdominal pain.

Common ingredients

Modeling clays for children are made of lightweight materials that are hardened by air contact. Other clays may need firing in a kiln or may not harden at all.

Ceramic clay minerals are composed of very small, plate-like particles formed by weathering of rocks such as **feldspar**. Water helps hold the particles together in sheets, and allows the particles to slide past each other without breaking apart, giving wet clay plasticity. Ceramic clay dries and hardens as the water evaporates but needs to be **fired** in high heat to dry completely.

Oil-based clays (Plasticine) are made with **calcium salts**, **petroleum jelly** and **waxy fats** that never dry out. They are used for clay **animation** as they allow figures to be repeatedly posed and reposed. Oil-based clays are somewhat **flammable**.

Polymer clays (Sculpey, FIMO) are made with PVC suspended in plasticizers and remain soft until they are **cured**, or heated to cause the polymer particles to swell and fuse together. **Fumes** released when polymer clays are accidently **burned** may be irritating but are not otherwise toxic.

Salt/flour doughs (Play-Doh, Crayola Dough) are lightweight air-hardening doughs marketed primarily for children. Most are made with wheat flour, but rice flour products are also available. Salt/flour doughs are easy to make at home.

Ceramic bead clays (Bubber) are made from polymer-coated microscopic ceramic beads. These clays are light and fluffy, never dry out and are easy to clean up.

Paper clay is any clay with cellulose fiber added, making it lighter and stronger. There is also a lightweight air-hardening product called Creative Paperclay that does not disclose its ingredients other than to say they are non-toxic.

What about Silly Putty?

Polydimethylsiloxane (PDMS), a flexible elastic silicone polymer used to fill breast implants, repair detached retinas and prevent oxidation in frying oil is the primary ingredient in Silly Putty®. Its entertaining qualities are due to the addition of **boron**, which creates temporary crosslinks between the chains of PDMS molecules, allowing it to be alternately flexible and stiff.

The substance that became trademarked as Silly Putty (also known as bouncing putty or science putty) was created accidentally in 1943 when a scientist trying to find an alternative to synthetic rubber mixed boric acid and silicone oil. Its usefulness went unappreciated for several years before someone realized it would make a fun toy. Since then people have put the putty to

myriad creative uses both on Earth and in space, where it can be used in zero gravity to hold tools in place.

Sadly, though, due to changes in inks and printing processes it can no longer be used to pick up images from the Sunday comics.

Crayola sells 5 lb. blocks of Silly Putty, and even larger quantities can be ordered from Dow Corning, where it is known as 3179 Dilatant Compound.

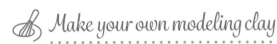

Make your own modeling clay

Saltflour dough

2 cups flour
1 cup salt
¾ cup water
2 tablespoons vegetable oil
Optional: Food coloring

» Stir dry ingredients together and then add wet ingredients. Knead until smooth.

To harden, air dry or place in oven that has been heated to 350 F and turned off.

Polymer clay

1 cup corn starch
1 cup white glue (polyvinyl acetate, PVA, such as Elmer's Glue All)
2 tablespoons mineral oil
1 tablespoon lemon juice
Optional: Tempera or acrylic paint for color

» Mix all ingredients and cook over low heat, stirring constantly, until dough forms.

» Allow to cool and then knead to desired consistency. Store in an airtight container.

To harden, air dry or bake in 180 F oven for 10 minutes.

Mold (food)

How toxic: Not toxic to toxic

Mouth	**Skin**	**Eyes**	**Inhalation**
Rarely toxic	*Not toxic*	*Not expected*	*May be irritating*
▼	▼		▼
Rinse mouth	Wash affected area		Fresh air

What to expect

Molds on food are usually not toxic unless a person is allergic. Mold spores may be a respiratory irritant.

See next page for information on handling moldy food.

Most food molds are pretty harmless when ingested, although some people may be **allergic** to them. Breathing in mold spores may cause respiratory irritation and sniffing moldy food is not recommended.

Molds are **fungi** and their life cycle is similar to that of **mushrooms**. Like mushrooms, food molds often grow deep below the surface and reproduce by sending stalks up into the air to release spores.

Whether or not moldy food is safe to eat depends on the food. **Soft foods** with high moisture content are less safe because they are easier for mold filaments to penetrate. **Harder foods** with lower moisture content are likely to have localized mold growths that can be cut away.

Whether keeping or discarding moldy food, be sure to clean the area where you were storing and handling it as it may have released spores that will contaminate nearby foods. **Refrigeration may slow but will not eliminate mold growth.**

Dangerous molds

Some fungi produce poisonous compounds called **mycotoxins**. In developed nations human illness from mycotoxins is rare, but there have been recalls of dog food and livestock feed due to contaminated grains.

Aflatoxins *Aspergillus flavus* and *Aspergillus parasiticus* can contaminate peanuts, corn, cottonseed and tree nuts both before and after harvest. Aflatoxins are associated with an increased risk of liver cancer.

Ergot *Claviceps purpurea* infects grasses and cereal grains, especially rye, when they are in bloom. It creates hardened capsules that replace grains on the stalk. Left behind at harvest they stay inactive through winter, then release spores in spring to infect the next crop.

Ergot infestation is so common that in earlier times the capsules were thought to be a normal part of the grain and were often consumed, resulting from time to time in mass outbreaks of ergot poisoning, known as **ergotism**. It is theorized that ergotism may have been behind some of the agitated behavior that led to the Salem witch trials.

Fumonisins *Fusarium moniliforme* and other *Fusarium* species infect corn both in the field and in storage. Fumonisins are known to have adverse effects, some severe, on livestock. Research has been inconclusive but they may be toxic to humans as well.

Vomitoxin (deoxynivalenol) *Fusarium graminearum* and *F. culmorum* cause **fusarium head blight** in wheat and **fusarium ear blight** in corn. It affects the quality of grain but is not known to cause illness unless consumed in very large quantities.

Preventing mold

Food molds are ubiquitous and it's impossible to avoid them altogether, but you can minimize exposure to them.

- » Launder kitchen towels and washcloths and replace sponges and mop heads frequently.
- » Clean countertops, cutting boards, storage containers and refrigerator regularly and keep them dry.
- » Keep foods, especially those with high moisture content, covered when serving.
- » Don't allow refrigerated foods to sit out longer than two hours.
- » Finish or discard leftovers within a few days of preparing.

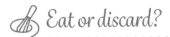 *Eat or discard?*

Moldy foods that should be discarded

- » Lunch meats, bacon, hot dogs
- » Cooked leftover meat and poultry
- » Cooked casseroles
- » Cooked grain and pasta
- » Soft cheese
- » Soft cheese made with mold, if it has mold that was not part of the manufacturing process
- » Yogurt and sour cream
- » Jams and jellies
- » Soft fruits and vegetables (cucumbers, peaches, tomatoes, etc.)
- » Bread and baked goods
- » Peanut butter, legumes and nuts

Moldy foods that may still be eaten

- » Hard salami and dry-cured country hams

  Surface mold is common; you can just scrub It off.

- » Hard cheese, whether or not mold was part of the manufacturing process

  Cut off at least 1 inch around and below the mold spot, keeping the knife out of the mold itself so it will not cross-contaminate other parts of the cheese.

  After trimming off the mold, re-cover the cheese in fresh wrap.

- » Firm fruits and vegetables (cabbage, bell peppers, carrots, etc.)

  Handle the same as hard cheese.

Mothballs

How toxic: Minimally toxic to highly toxic

Mouth	**Skin**	**Eyes**	**Inhalation**
Serious toxicity is possible ▼ Rinse mouth	*Serious toxicity is possible* ▼ Wash affected area	*May be irritating* ▼ Irrigate	*Serious toxicity is possible* ▼ Fresh air

What to expect

Accidental ingestion of mothballs is unlikely due to their strong, unpleasant odor. A taste is likely to be irritating and may cause nausea.

Intentional ingestion or inhalation of mothballs can result in severe toxicity. See below for more information.

Warning

Intentional inhalation or ingestion of mothballs can result in hemolytic anemia and damage to the brain, liver, lungs and eyes.

Naphthalene and paradichlorobenzene (PDCB) are pesticides that work as fumigants. They **sublimate** (change directly from solid to gas) readily and their gases kill moths in all phases of their life cycle.

Items stored with mothballs must be kept in **tightly sealed** containers for the fumes to remain concentrated enough to kill moths. Mothballs can soften plastics such as buttons if stored in direct contact.

Inhalation of fumes due to excessive use of mothballs inside the home can cause significant toxicity, as can inhalation and skin contact from clothing stored in mothballs. **They should not be used for diapers, infant clothing or baby blankets.**

Naphthalene and PDCB are highly effective but have several drawbacks, including their strong, persistent odors and potential toxicity.

Naphthalene is a petroleum derivative and is highly flammable. It's also a common product of combustion and is released into the environment not only when coal and oil are burned, but also through burning of wood and other biomass, and even through cooking some foods (mostly meats) at high temperatures.

Naphthalene is toxic through ingestion, inhalation and skin contact. It can cause a number of symptoms but is most known for causing **hemolytic anemia**, in which red blood cells are destroyed.

Paradichlorobenzene, PDCB, is considered less toxic than napthalene but is still a potent **neurotoxin** when ingested or inhaled. It can cause **leukoencephalopathy**, or destruction of the white matter of the brain.

Preventing moth infestation

» Launder or dry clean items before storage, then pack in an airtight bag or bin.

» Take woolen coats and shoes outside and thoroughly brush to remove any eggs or larvae that may be present.

» Thoroughly clean resale shop or yard sale items containing animal fibers before putting them in with other clothing.

» Place items that can't be laundered or dry cleaned in ziplock bags and freeze for two weeks.

» Vacuum wool rugs regularly. Be sure no edges are turned under and don't overlook areas that are under furniture.

About clothes moths

Moths seen out in the open air of the house are usually **pantry moths**, as clothes moths prefer warm, dark, hidden places. When clothes moths are disturbed they are more likely to run or hop than fly.

Clothes moths are attracted to animal fibers of all kinds, including wool, silk, fur and feathers, and in any form including clothing, carpets, down comforters and even fur and dander shed by pets.

They lay their eggs on the fibers so the **larvae**, or worms, that hatch can start feeding right away. All damage is done by the larvae as the the **adult moths don't eat.**

Alternatives to mothballs

Less toxic alternatives also tend to be less effective.and should be considered an adjunct to regular cleaning and proper storage.

Pheromone traps lure male moths to prevent them mating. They will have no effect on females, eggs or larvae.

Permethrin spray can be applied directly to clothing. Test for staining first.

Deltamethrin dust must be applied with care and only to cracks and crevices where moth larvae go to pupate, or transform into their adult form. Deltamethrin is much more toxic than other pyrethroids (p. 91).

Dry ice (p. 76) can be used to fumigate infested items. Wrap ½ pound to one pound dry ice in a cloth and place in the bottom of a heavy-weight trash bag. Place clothing items in the bag and close it, leaving a small opening for the gas to escape. Once the ice has completely vaporized keep the bag tightly sealed for another 3 to 4 days.

Lavender and essential oils have some repellent effect but won't kill moths in any phase of the life cycle.

Cedar balls, blocks and chests work as repellents and may also kill some larvae. To maintain their effectiveness cedar products should be refreshed from time to time, either by sanding or by rubbing with cedar oil.

Mouthwash

How toxic: Not toxic to toxic

Mouth	**Skin**	**Eyes**	**Inhalation**
May be intoxicating if alcohol-based ▼ Rinse mouth	*Not toxic* ▼ Wash affected area	*May be irritating* ▼ Irrigate	*Not expected*

What to expect

Ingestion of non-alcohol mouthwash in large amounts may upset the stomach, and if it contains sorbitol diarrhea is possible. These symptoms should be mild and limited.

Alcohol-containing mouthwash is potentially toxic as the alcohol content may be up to 30%. Poison control can help calculate a potential blood alcohol concentration.

Common ingredients

Mouthwashes are classified as either cosmetic or therapeutic. Cosmetic mouthwashes mask mouth odor with fragrances, whereas therapeutic products help reduce plaque, gingivitis and tooth decay.

Cetylpyridinium chloride is a cationic detergent that kills a broad spectrum of oral bacteria. It then neutralizes pro-inflammatory toxins released from the damaged bacterial cells that would otherwise cause gingivitis.

Sodium hexametaphosphate is a phosphorus compound that helps protect teeth from staining both from foods and beverages and from cetylpyridinium chloride, which can discolor teeth.

Hydrogen peroxide (p. 118) whitens teeth through its bleaching action.

Stabilized chlorine dioxide is actually **sodium chlorite**. Chlorine dioxide is a gas that is synthesized by reacting chlorine compounds with various other substances. Chlorine dioxide is a powerful disinfectant and neutralizes smelly sulfur compounds that cause bad breath, but it's also quite toxic. Buffered with various carbonates, chlorine dioxide is transformed to sodium chlorite, which is less toxic but also less effective. Dentists sell two-part products that include sodium chlorite and an activator, which are mixed together just before use to form true chlorine dioxide.

Zinc chloride both kills germs and binds sulfur compounds so we can't smell them. It is often combined synergistically with cetylpyridinium chloride and sodium chlorite. Zinc rinses may contain polymers that adhere it to teeth so it keeps neutralizing odors for several hours.

Enzymes that not only help digest food but also keep bacteria populations in check are normally provided by saliva. When a medical condition decreases saliva production, a dry-mouth rinse can be used that contains some of those same enzymes. These mouthwashes are likely to also contain humectants like **propylene glycol**.

Methyl salicylate, also known as **wintergreen oil**, combined with other essential oils forms the basis for Listerine®, the makers of which invented the term **halitosis** so their product could be proposed as its cure. Methyl salicylate is chemically related to **aspirin** and ingestion of pure wintergreen oil can be fatal, but the amount in mouthwash is much too small to be toxic even if ingested in large quantities.

Eucalyptol, **thymol**, and **menthol** are additional essential oils that are antimicrobial and have pleasing flavors.

Ethanol is used in mouthwash as an antimicrobial, solvent and preservative. Mouthwashes with high alcohol content tend to cause an acute burning sensation and may leave the mouth feeling dry. They should be kept well out of reach of children, adults with cognitive impairments and those who struggle with alcohol addiction.

There have been conflicting studies on whether ethanol mouthwashes can cause **cancer**, and we just don't know. Poor dental hygiene, smoking and drinking alcohol are known to increase cancer risk. Rinsing with an alcohol mouthwash three or more times per day may also increase risk, but that kind of use is unusual. It may be that those who use mouthwash excessively do so because they have poor hygiene or because they smoke and drink.

 *Make your own mouthwash*

Essential oils

Essential oils can be added to water, ethanol or a combination of the two. Rubbing alcohol should never be used in the mouth.

Essential oils with antimicrobial properties include:

- » Peppermint
- » Wintergreen
- » Cinnamon
- » Thyme
- » Oregano
- » Salvia
- » Clove
- » Tea tree
- » Eucalyptus

Sore mouth rinse

1 cup warm water
¼ teaspoon baking soda
⅛ teaspoon salt

Hydrogen peroxide

Dilute 3% peroxide with an equal amount of plain water. Rinse with water afterward to avoid dry mouth. If your mouth still feels dry you can stimulate saliva by chewing sugarless gum.

Nail polish

How toxic: Not toxic

Mouth	**Skin**	**Eyes**	**Inhalation**
Not toxic	*Not toxic*	*May be irritating*	*Not expected*
▼	▼	▼	
Rinse mouth	Wash affected area	Irrigate	

What to expect

Children may put a nail polish brush in their mouth or paint their lips but ingestion is unlikely. Polish that dries and sticks to teeth is not toxic and will wear off on its own.

Nail polish remover (see page 142) should not be used in or around the mouth, or on large areas of skin.

Common ingredients

Individual formulas vary, but all nail polishes are made of polymer film formers, plasticizers to keep them supple and solvents to keep them liquid. Other ingredients are added to adjust texture and to add color and other effects.

Nitrocellulose, also known as **cellulose nitrate**, is the primary film former in nail polish. It is produced by treating cellulose to give it a higher nitrogen content. The cellulose can be taken from cotton fibers but is more commonly derived from wood pulp. The more nitrogen the compound contains the more flammable it is, and highly nitrated nitrocellulose, known as **guncotton**, is used in explosives, rocket fuels and gunpowder. Nitrocellulose is also used to make flash paper for magic tricks, and its ability to trap and hold proteins has made it a common substrate for urine pregnancy tests. The nitrocellulose used in nail polish has has a safe nitrogen content, and while care must be taken in the manufacturing process it won't be explosive in the home.

Modified cellulose polymers such as **cellulose acetate** and **methyl cellulose** are produced, as is nitrocellulose, by treating cellulose to create long repeating chains of molecules called polymers. Their binding, emulsifying and film-forming qualities make them useful additions to a vast number of products including packaging and construction materials, foods and personal care products.

Tosylamide/formaldehyde resin works with nitrocellulose, which is naturally brittle, to form a more durable film and to adhere well to the nail. Despite its name the resin contains no more than trace amounts of the formaldehyde used in its production. Confusion over this causes alarm, though, and some companies use **tosylamide/epoxy resin** instead.

Solvents keep nail polish liquid; it dries as the solvents evaporate. Common solvents include **ethyl acetate, butyl acetate** and **propyl acetate**, some of which occur naturally in various fruits and all of which are used as fragrances and flavoring agents. **Isopropyl alcohol** (p. 156) is a solvent that also stabilizes nitrocellulose to make it less flammable. **Toluene** was once common in nail polish but has fallen out of favor due to concerns about its toxicity.

Plasticizers such as **triphenylphosphate** and **camphor** keep the film formers flexible by squeezing in between the polymers' molecule chains and lubricating them so they don't settle into rigid frameworks.

Photoinitiators such as **benzoyl peroxide** are the reason gel polishes must be cured under UV light. They absorb energy from the light and set off a chemical reaction in the film-forming polymers, causing the chains of molecules to form into crosslinked networks. Only the photoinitiators that are in direct contact with the light react in this way, so each layer of polish must be cured.

UV absorbers such as **benzophenone** absorb and disperse UV rays so they don't affect the color of the polish. They are used in many other personal care products, including sunscreens (p. 164) where they help protect skin from sun damage.

Pigments include dyes and ingredients that add sparkle and other special effects. **Lakes** are dyes that have been bound to a metal salt to make them durable, fade-resistant and compatible with the other ingredients. **Mica** is a shiny silicate mineral. **Bismuth oxychloride** has a pearlescent sheen.

Coloring nails with henna

Henna from the *Lawsonia inermis* plant colors and strengthens nails, although the range of orange-to-red color you can achieve is limited. Henna provides a persistent stain that lasts until nails grow out. Be sure to buy only pure henna powder as adulterated products can be dangerous.

To use

» Mix 1 tablespoon henna powder with just enough lemon juice to make a thick paste.

» Cover and place in refrigerator for 6 to 12 hours.

» Wipe nails with vinegar, isopropyl alcohol or nail polish remover and let dry.

» Apply petroleum jelly or white glue to cuticles and skin around nails to prevent staining, then apply henna paste thickly to nails.

» Leave for one hour (longer if darker stain is desired), then remove by wiping with lemon juice or apple cider vinegar. Process may be repeated to build up more intense color.

» Add a top coat of clear polish if desired; otherwise, avoid getting nails wet for 12 hours.

Nail polish remover

How toxic: Not toxic to toxic

Mouth	**Skin**	**Eyes**	**Inhalation**
Rarely toxic	*May be irritating with prolonged exposure*	*May be irritating*	*Toxic when abused*
▼	▼	▼	▼
Rinse mouth, eat milk chocolate	Wash affected area	Irrigate	See page 19

What to expect

Acetone products contain a bittering agent that leaves a terrible taste; milk chocolate is the only known antidote.

Inhalation abuse of acetone can lead to severe injury. Non-acetone products are generally not toxic.

Common ingredients

Nail polish removers contain solvents that re-liquify the polish so it can be wiped away. Non-acetone removers often use the same solvents that are in nail polish itself.

Acetone is an effective solvent for plastics, and because nail polish is basically a plastic film spread over nails, acetone is the most effective nail polish remover. It can be toxic when ingested and drying to nails, so alternatives are available.

Acetone is commonly present in the environment due to manmade pollutants like cigarette smoke and automobile exhaust, and to natural occurrences such as forest fires and volcanic eruptions.

We all inhale and ingest some amount of acetone on a daily basis, and acetone is also produced in our bodies as a byproduct of fat metabolism.

Because it can be toxic when ingested in highly concentrated products like nail polish remover, a bittering agent called **denatonium** (more on next page) is added to make it nearly impossible to swallow.

The worst side effect from acetone nail polish remover ingestion is likely to be the extremely unpleasant taste it leaves in the mouth. Rinsing with water may help some but according to the manufacturer the only known antidote is **milk chocolate**. If you have no chocolate on hand you'll just have to wait for the taste to resolve on its own.

Methyl oleate is derived from fatty acids that may be of animal or vegetable origin. It is marketed as an all-natural, non-toxic nail polish remover. It is of very low toxicity, is biodegradable, and is used as a solvent, emollient and emulsifier in a variety of personal care products and commercial processes.

Methyl ethyl acetate, also known as **butanone**, is found naturally in some fruits and other foods, but for commercial purposes it's derived from an alcohol called

2-butanol. It's one of the solvents that is also used to keep nail polish liquid in the bottle.

Ethyl acetate is made by reacting ethanol with acetic acid. It has a characteristic sweet smell and is used as a flavoring agent in candy, baked goods and perfumes. It's another solvent that is used to keep nail polish liquid until it dries.

Acetonitrile, also known as **methyl cyanide**, was once commonly used to dissolve artificial nail glue and other household glues.

It is less common now because acetonitrile breaks down into cyanide in the body and ingestion can be fatal. Be extremely cautious if you have any products in your home that contain acetonitrile.

About denatonium

Denatonium, famous as the world's bitterest known substance, is most commonly found in household products in the form of **denatonium benzoate** or **denatonium saccharide**. It was discovered accidentally in 1958 by a Scottish pharmaceutical company experimenting with **lidocaine**, which is chemically very similar. Denatonium can be detected by the human tongue in extremely small amounts and is so aggressively unpalatable that adding just a little to a potentially toxic product makes ingestion nearly impossible.

According to the manufacturer of **Bitrex®** (denatonium benzoate), **milk chocolate** is the only antidote for its bitter taste. The company (bitrex.com) helpfully offers taste test kits so you can get a group together and discover just how awful it is.

Alternatives to nail polish remover

Nail polish

Liquid nail polish in the bottle contains solvents that evaporate as the polish dries. Brush wet polish on over dry and wipe them both away with a paper towel.

Multi-purpose white glue (such as Elmer's)

Mix one part white glue to two parts water and brush on nails before polish. Allow the glue to dry and apply polish as usual. When ready to remove, peel the glue and polish off together. This is especially helpful for hard-to-remove glitter polish.

Alcohol (ethanol and isopropyl)

Neither is a very effective solvent for nail polish, but with patience and determination they may work for you. You might also try products like hairspray or cologne that have alcohol in them.

Hot water

Soak nails in hot water until polish softens, then rub with a dry cloth.

Oven cleaners

How toxic: Minimally toxic to toxic

Mouth	**Skin**	**Eyes**	**Inhalation**
May be irritating	*May be irritating*	*May cause injury*	*May be irritating*
▼	▼	▼	▼
Rinse mouth	Wash affected area	Irrigate for 30 minutes	Fresh air

What to expect

Pain or blisters in the mouth are not expected after ingestion and would require medical attention. Throat pain or trouble swallowing needs evaluation even if the mouth looks fine.

Eyes should be irrigated for 30 minutes after any oven cleaner exposure. Medical evaluation is needed for pain or vision changes that persist after irrigation.

Common ingredients

Oven cleaners use some of the same ingredients as degreasers.
Like degreasers, oven cleaners seldom cause significant injury,
but they are more likely to emit fumes that can be irritating.

Sodium hydroxide, or lye, is extremely alkaline and saponifies, or converts into soap, grease and greasy residue in the oven, making it easy to wipe away. It is produced by running electrical current through a solution of sodium chloride (table salt) in water. Historically lye was produced by soaking wood ash in water.

Potassium carbonate is a strong alkali used in low-fume products in place of sodium hydroxide. A predecessor of baking soda, it is also known as **pearlash** and was once produced by baking impurities out of potash; nowadays it is more commonly produced from potassium chloride, which occurs as a mineral called **silvite**. It is used to dutch-process cocoa, making the cocoa darker and mellower in flavor.

Diethylene glycol monobutyl ether is a mutual solvent that can dissolve both water- and oil-based substances so they can all wash away together.

Sodium lauroyl sarcosinate is a surfactant derived from the amino acid **sarcosine**, which occurs naturally in many vegetables and animals (humans included), although it can also be synthesized.

It has no known toxicity and is used in many cleaning and personal care products because in addition to its surfactant qualities it also is a foam builder; in oven cleaners this helps the product stick to the sides of the oven.

Hydrotreated light petroleum distillates are a mixture of solvents derived from petroleum products. They are deodorized by reacting them with hydrogen to remove smelly nitrogen and sulfur compounds.

Ethanolamines are used as pH adjusters to keep products alkaline, because alkaline substances are best for dissolving, or saponifying, oils and grease.

They may also have detergent and emulsification properties.

Ethanolamines are incorporated into biological processes in both plant and animal cells. Antihistamines like diphenhydramine (Benadryl®) and doxylamine (Unisom®) are also ethanolamines.

Alternatives to oven cleaning products

Aluminum foil

Covering the floor of an electric oven with aluminum foil helps keep spills from accumulating, as does covering the lowest rack in any kind of oven. However, you should never cover the vent holes on the bottom of a gas oven, as this can cause carbon monoxide (p. 52) to build up.

Ammonia

This method can be used in any kind of oven, but with a gas oven you must first turn off the pilot light and gas supply. Ammonia fumes can become explosive when mixed with air and gas in a confined space.

- » Heat the oven to 150 F (65 C) and turn it off.
- » Place a large pan of boiling water on the bottom rack and a bowl or dish containing ½ cup ammonia on the top rack. Allow to sit overnight.
- » In the morning remove the pan of water and the bowl of ammonia and leave the door open to allow the oven to air out.
- » After airing, add the ammonia and a few drops of hand dishwashing soap to a quart of warm water and use it to wipe out the softened residue.
- » Soak racks in hot water and ammonia for 15 minutes, then rinse and wipe.

Baking soda

- » Coat the inside of the oven with a paste of baking soda and water and allow to sit over night.
- » Wipe the paste off the next day with a wet sponge, using vinegar water if desired.

Salt

- » Sprinkle salt over food spills in the oven as soon as they happen, then wipe the residue up after the oven has cooled.
- » Mix salt and lemon juice 1:1. Scrub where needed and wipe clean.

Paint (interior & exterior)

How toxic: Not toxic to minimally toxic except old lead-based paints

Mouth	**Skin**	**Eyes**	**Inhalation**
Not toxic (unless lead-based)	*Not toxic*	*May be irritating*	*VOC fumes can be irritating*
▼	▼	▼	▼
Rinse mouth	Wash affected area	Irrigate	Avoid use; fresh air

What to expect

A taste of paint is not expected to cause any specific symptoms and a larger ingestion is very unlikely. VOCs given off as paint dries can cause headaches, nausea and eye, nose and throat irritation. Ingestion of lead paints made prior to 1978 that have peeled off walls or have been sanded can cause severe, lasting neurological damage.

Common ingredients

Concerns that volatile organic compounds (VOCs) emitted by paints may cause health problems have led to development of low- or no-VOC paints. Not all VOCs have noticeable odors and a high-VOC paint will not necessarily have a strong smell.

Prime pigments, also known as **hiding** pigments, are finely ground solid particles that bounce light off the paint so you can't see what's under it. **Titanium dioxide** is the most commonly used white pigment but **zinc compounds** are also used.

Color pigments, both organic (containing carbon, such as **pthalocyanine**) and inorganic (containing no carbon, such as **iron oxide**), add color by absorbing some wavelengths of light and reflecting others. Pigment particles scatter light in irregular patterns and a higher concentration of pigment to binder gives paint a matte finish.

Extender pigments like clay, silica and talc add no color. They are used to add bulk, limit gloss, and enhance texture and adhesion.

Binders hold pigment particles together and form a film to adhere them to the painted surface. They reflect light in regular patterns and a higher concentration of binder to pigment will give the paint more sheen. **Polyvinyl acetate** (white glue) is a common binder for water-based paints. **Synthetic resins** are used as binders for **alkyds**, previously called **oil-based** paints.

Solvents keep other ingredients liquid enough to be spread. After paint is applied to a surface the solvent evaporates and leaves the pigment and binder behind. Paints with resin binders generally require solvents made from **volatile organic compounds** (VOCs). Latex (acrylic) binders use water as a solvent. New formulas called **alkyd emulsions** have been developed that allow alkyds to be dispersed in water.

Volatile organic compounds

Many solvents that keep paint liquid before use and then evaporate as the paint dries are volatile organic compounds (VOCs). In this context **organic** means they contain carbon, and **volatile** means they easily turn to gas or vapor at normal room temperatures.

The VOCs used in oil-based or alkyd paints tend to give them a characteristic strong odor, but they can continue to off-gas long after the paint dries and the smell is no longer noticeable. VOCs are also emitted by other synthetic household materials such as carpeting, vinyl flooring and composite woods, as well as some cleaning and personal care products, tobacco smoke and even fumes from cooking.

Not all VOCs are toxic, but some are known or suspected carcinogens. Short-term exposure to some can cause headaches, nausea and nose, throat and eye irritation, and long-term exposure can affect the liver, kidneys and central nervous system.

As with other toxins, VOCs pose the most risk to the very young, the very old and those with pre-existing medical conditions such as asthma. Pregnant women are usually advised to avoid VOCs.

Low- or zero-VOC paints are available. There is no legal standard for low-VOC labeling, but a generally accepted standard is that a low-VOC product should contain less than 50 grams of VOCs per liter. Paints branded as zero-VOC are generally presumed to contain less than 5 grams of VOCs per liter. Pigments added to paint in the store may contain VOCs of their own and may raise the VOC level of the paint you take home.

Latex paints with matte or low-gloss finishes and lighter colors are usually going to be lowest in VOCs. Paints sold for exterior surfaces are likely to be higher in VOCs, and this is an excellent reason to avoid using exterior paint inside your home.

Lead paint

Lead was once common in paint because it is opaque, durable and highly water-resistant. It's also highly toxic and was banned in the US in 1978. Many homes built before then will have been painted with lead paint at some time.

Over time lead paint becomes brittle and peels, creating a grave danger to children who pull pieces off walls or trim and eat them. Sanding into old layers of lead paint creates a fresh danger and can contaminate the surrounding property as well.

Lead is particularly dangerous for young children, as the damage it wreaks on their developing brains is irreversible. Lead can accumulate in bones and pose a danger long after exposure has ended.

Lead paint can be safely painted over but should be removed with great care, a job best left to professionals.

How to dispose of paint

Leftover paint should be left uncovered to dry completely before being discarded. Check with your waste management company to see if you can put it out with your regular trash.

Latex paint can be recycled. Check **paintcare.org** to see if your state has drop-off locations.

Pepper spray & other defense sprays

How toxic: Toxic to very toxic

Mouth	**Skin**	**Eyes**	**Inhalation**
Irritating, may cause vomiting	*Irritating*	*Severely irritating*	*Severely irritating*
▼	▼	▼	▼
Rinse mouth	Wash affected area	Irrigate	Fresh air

What to expect

Pepper sprays incapacitate by forcing the eyes closed and causing breath to turn quick and shallow. These distressing effects usually resolve in under an hour, but less intense discomfort may continue for hours afterward.

Eye pain, vision changes, trouble breathing or swallowing or blistering of skin require medical attention. Tear gas, especially CN (chloroacetophenone), can be much more dangerous than pepper spray.

Warning

Rubbing skin or eyes after pepper spray exposure increases burning, spreads contamination and may cause injury. Touching the face, eyes or other affected areas should be avoided. Decontamination should be done under running water with the least friction possible.

Common ingredients

Capsaicin-based pepper sprays can be used to deter attacks by dogs, bears and other animals, but tear gases are only effective on humans.

Oleoresin capsicum (OC) is an oily extract of the **capsicum annuum chili pepper** that is used in hot sauces, topical pain relievers and pepper spray. OC is a complex mix of chemicals known as **capsaicin and related capsaicinoids**.

The **major capsaicinoids** (MC) are **capsaicin** and **dihydrocapsaicin**, and it is the percentage of MC in the spray that determines how much the spray burns. Increasing the concentration of OC in the canister makes the effects last longer but doesn't make them stronger.

Research has shown that a single exposure to pepper spray causes no lasting injury but that repeated exposures may damage the eyes and respiratory tract. Because pepper spray inflames the airway it can be dangerous for those with **asthma** or other respiratory conditions.

OC sprays have been shown to be effective against bears, dogs and other attacking animals, as well as humans under the influence of stimulants and other drugs.

Chloroacetophenone (CN) is a lacrimator or **tear gas**, which are general terms for substances that irritate the eyes and cause them to water. It is not a gas at all but rather a **solid** dissolved in a solvent. It's the most toxic tear gas and while mild exposures are temporarily incapacitating, severe exposures can cause injury and illness. Due to differences in anatomy CN is not effective as an animal repellent. CN is the lacrimator that was first known as **Mace**. It is outlawed in some states.

Chlorobenzylidene-malononitrile (CS) has largely replaced CN as it is considered to be both more potent and less toxic. Like CN, CS is not a gas but is an aerosolized solid. Some people have a natural immunity to CS and it doesn't work very well against people who are intoxicated, under the influence of stimulants or enraged. Although it is considered less toxic than CN, a severe or prolonged exposure to CS can still lead to permanent eye injury or even death.

Marking dye is added to 3-in-1 sprays that contain both OC and tear gas (either CS or CN) so an attacker can be identified later even if they run away. Some dyes glow under ultraviolet light, others are visible in normal light.

What is Mace?

In the 1960s a Pittsburgh inventor came up with a way to package CN in a pocket-size canister that could be safely carried for personal protection. He called it **Chemical Mace**, a reference to a type of medieval spiked weapon. Chemical Mace was later sold to Smith and Wesson, and then transferred to a company that became what is now known as Mace Security International. The company sells a wide range of products including OC sprays as well as 3-in-1 sprays containing OC, CN and UV marking dye.

 Cleaning up pepper spray & other defense sprays

See jalapeno peppers, page 122, for personal decontamination and treatment options.

Pepper spray

After a small indoor pepper spray discharge, just opening the windows and airing the place out may suffice. Care should be taken if residue from the spray settles into carpets, curtains or other fabrics; they they may need to be handled by professionals. There are numerous companies that specialize in hazardous cleanups.

OC is an oily resin, so cleaning hard surfaces requires washing with a grease-cutting detergent made for dishes or clothing. Gloves are a must.

Tear gas

CS and CN are aerosolized solids, so they will leave behind a powdery residue that needs to be wetted down before it is wiped off. Household vacuum cleaners should not be used as they may blow the powder back into the air.

Perfume, cologne & other fragrances

How toxic: Not toxic to toxic

Mouth	**Skin**	**Eyes**	**Inhalation**
Intoxicating in large quantities ▼ Rinse mouth	*Not toxic* ▼ Wash affected area	*May be irritating* ▼ Irrigate	*Sensitivity reactions may occur*

What to expect

Most fragrance products contain ethanol and could be intoxicating if ingested in quantity, but the addition of bittering agents makes ingestion unlikely. Milk chocolate may help with the bitter taste. Medical evaluation would be needed in the event of a large ingestion.

Common ingredients

The word perfume is derived from *per fumum*, Latin for *by or through smoke*.
It originally referred to incense burned during religious ceremonies.

Fragrances may be derived from oils or extracts of flowers, leaves, fruit or other natural sources, or may be synthetic. Not all scents found in nature can be extracted from the source, and those that can may be too variable or unstable to produce consistent results. **Headspace technology** involves placing a fragrant object or substance in an airtight chamber and pulling off its scent compounds so they can be analyzed and reproduced.

Ethanol is the most common fragrance diluent because it has no competing scent and it evaporates from the skin quickly, leaving the perfume essence behind. The ethanol itself is usually diluted with a small percentage (2% to 4%) of water to slow its evaporation just a little, as some scent molecules will be carried away with the alcohol as it dries.

Isopropyl myristate is composed of isopropyl alcohol (p. 156) and **myristic acid**, a fatty acid first isolated from nutmeg. It is easily absorbed by skin and carries fragrance molecules along with it, making the scent last longer.

Monopropylene glycol, another term for propylene glycol, is a cosolvent that helps keep fragrance oils dissolved in ethanol and water.

T-butyl alcohol is a solvent that also works as a **denaturant** or bittering agent to make ethanol unpalatable.

Denatonium benzoate (p. 143) is the bitterest substance known. It is used to denature many products with high alcohol contents.

Scents & receptors

When we breathe in, inhaled air goes up our nostrils to an air-filled space called the **nasal cavity**, where it is cleaned, warmed and humidified before it continues down the airway.

The nasal cavity also contains a postage-stamp-sized patch of about 6 million specialized cells called **olfactory receptors** (dogs, by comparison, have 300 million olfactory receptors). When an odorant binds to and stimulates an olfactory receptor, a message is sent to the brain that is interpreted as a scent. Which scent the brain detects depends on the combination and number of receptors stimulated.

Indole, for example, is an odorant that occurs naturally both in **feces** and in **orange blossoms**. If many receptors are flooded with indole we perceive an extremely offensive odor, but if just a few receptors are stimulated we perceive a pleasant flowery smell.

Unscented vs fragrance-free

Unscented products do, of course, have a scent, because it would be impossible to create a mixture that didn't bind to a single olfactory receptor. In these products, each ingredient that has a noticeable odor is countered with another ingredient that neutralizes that odor.

A product that is **fragrance-free** has not had anything added for the specific purpose of creating a scent, but its ingredients may have detectable odors of their own.

What's the difference?

Fragrance products are made of proprietary blends of odorants, both natural and synthetic, known as **perfume essences**.

These essences tend to be overpowering in their pure form and so they are diluted to various degrees. This dilution can also separate the different scents in the mix so they don't hit your nose in one big jumble. Fragrances are classified according to how **concentrated** they are.

Perfume, also called parfum, is the most concentrated fragrance. It is typically 20% to 30% perfume essence. Its scent may linger for up to 24 hours.

Eau de perfume/parfum contains about 15% to 20% perfume essence and lasts about eight hours.

Eau de toilette contains about 5% to 15% perfume essence and lasts about three hours. In this context *toilette* is taken from the French term for the process of preparing oneself for the coming day.

Cologne is short for eau de Cologne. It contains 2% to 5% perfume essence and lasts for about two hours. Named for a light, fruity fragrance that originated in the German city of Cologne, in the US it generally refers to fresh, woody or musky products for men, although it may also be applied to a highly diluted version of a more concentrated fragrance.

Petroleum jelly

How toxic: Not toxic

Mouth	Skin	Eyes	Inhalation
Not toxic	*Not toxic*	*May be irritating*	*Not expected*
▼	▼	▼	
Rinse mouth	Wash affected area	Irrigate	

What to expect

Petroleum jelly is not toxic although a large ingestion could lubricate the GI tract and cause mild diarrhea.

It can be hard to remove petroleum jelly from hair and fabrics; suggestions are given on the next page.

Petroleum jelly, also known as **petrolatum** and **soft paraffin**, is derived from petroleum oil. Crude oil is a complex mix of hydrocarbons that can be separated into many different substances. After lighter components have been removed a thick gel is left behind that is filtered, purified and made into petroleum jelly.

Native Americans found various uses for crude oil they found seeping into local waterways, from basket waterproofing to wound care. The Seneca Indians in upstate New York sold it to early settlers as they arrived and it became known as **Seneca oil**. In the mid-19th century underground oil reserves were discovered in Pennsylvania, spurring an industry based on separating the crude into its useful components.

The chemist Robert Chesebrough, who had previously worked on deriving kerosene from whale oil, found oil workers rubbing a sticky oil residue into their wounds and spent years figuring out how to isolate and purify it. He called the light-colored, odorless product **Wonder Jelly**, later changing the name to **Vaseline®**. Chesebrough lived to be 96 and is said to have taken a spoonful of Vaseline by mouth every day. While petroleum jelly is not absorbed through the GI tract, internal use is no longer recommended.

When Vaseline was brought to market it was extolled as a cure-all that could treat everything from dry skin to coughs to hair loss. It quickly replaced lard in pharmaceutical preparations and hair pomades, because unlike animal fats it has little taste or smell and never turns rancid.

Petroleum jelly is not the panacea Chesebrough thought it was but it does have a number of legitimate uses. It isn't absorbed into skin and doesn't really soften it; instead it creates a smooth barrier over the skin that can keep irritants out while holding moisture in.

Cosmetic- and pharmaceutical-grade petroleum jelly is called **petrolatum USP**. Products not so labeled may contain dangerous impurities.

Removing petroleum jelly from fabric

» Use a spoon or butter knife to pick up as much of the jelly as possible. Work toward the center to keep from spreading it, and use a scooping motion to lift it off the fabric rather than rubbing it in.

» Blot with a paper towel until the towel comes away clean.

» Work cornstarch gently into the fabric, allow to sit for at least one hour and then brush off or vacuum.

» Repeat as necessary. If the fabric is washable you can follow up with a degreasing hand dishwashing soap.

Removing petroleum jelly from hair

Before it can be washed out petroleum jelly must be dissolved by a less tenacious vegetable oil, such as olive or canola.

» Work the vegetable oil into the jelly, thoroughly breaking it up.

» Cover the hair, jelly and oil with degreasing hand dishwashing soap, lather well and rinse.

» Repeat as needed.

Make your own petroleum jelly alternative

Recipes for making petroleum jelly alternatives at home are generally variations on mixing vegetable oil and beeswax, with optional vitamin E or essential oils.

With beeswax

4 parts vegetable oil (such as olive, almond, sunflower or coconut, or a mix)
1 part beeswax
Optional: Vitamin E, essential oils

» Melt beeswax in pot, double boiler or microwave.

» Mix in oil.

» Pour into a clean container and allow to cool.

Vegan alternative

1 part cocoa butter
1 part vegetable oil
Optional: Vitamin E, essential oils

» Melt together, stir and allow to cool.

Pool chemicals

How toxic: Not toxic to toxic

Mouth	**Skin**	**Eyes**	**Inhalation**
May be irritating	*May be drying*	*May be irritating*	*May be irritating*
▼	▼	▼	▼
Rinse mouth	Wash affected area	Irrigate	Fresh air

What to expect

Ingestion Mild throat irritation is common. Children may have more severe symptoms. Coughing, drooling, pain or difficulty swallowing requires medical attention.

Inhalation Chlorine gas is sharply irritating to eyes, nose, throat and lungs and may trigger asthma. Breathing steam is very soothing to the respiratory tract.

Warning
Chlorine is a strong oxidizer and pool supplies containing chlorine in any form must be stored and handled with care. See "Pool chemical safety" on opposite page for more information.

Common ingredients

Chlorine is the most common pool disinfectant, but there are alternatives. A number of additional chemicals are used to keep water clean and clear.

Hypochlorites dissociate in water and form hypochlorous acid (HOCl), an effective biocide that also occurs naturally in our bodies, as white blood cells employ it to destroy bacteria and viruses.

The hypochlorous acid in pool water that is available for attacking pathogens is called **free chlorine**. Once it has reacted with contaminants in the water it becomes **combined chlorine**, which is much less effective.

Calcium hypochlorite is made by treating lime with chlorine gas and is provided in solid form (tablets or granules). It has to be dissolved in water before use.

Sodium hypochlorite (p. 42) comes in liquid form. It is formulated to provide more free chlorine than household bleach.

Lithium hypochlorite is a powder that dissolves easily in water and is kinder to pool linings and hardware than other hypochlorites. Lithium, a metal that is mined from deposits around the world, may become more expensive and less readily available for pool use due to increasing demand for lithium batteries (p. 41).

TriChlor (trichloroisocyanuric acid) and **DiChlor** (dichloroisocyanuric acid) are hypochlorites that are stabilized with **cyanuric acid** (see next page).

Bromine compounds dissociate in water to form hypobromous acid. Hypobromous acid reacts with organic matter to form bromamines, but they are not toxic. Hypobromous acid is more readily degraded by UV rays than hypochlorous acid and can't be stabilized with cyanuric acid, so it is used for indoor pools, especially hot tubs.

Sodium chloride Salt water pools use electrolysis to split sodium chloride and water into hydrogen and hypochlorous acid, which converts back into water and sodium chloride. Once an appropriate salt level is obtained it seldom needs to be adjusted.

Other chemicals

Calcium chloride is added to soft water to raise calcium levels. When there's too little calcium in pool water it will leach calcium from the pool's plaster lining, and can cause a vinyl lining to lose its elasticity.

Cyanuric acid is a weak acid that doesn't affect the pH of pool water. It bonds with free chlorine and absorbs UV rays, protecting the chlorine from degradation. This leaves the chlorine's disinfection power intact but does slow it some. Cyanuric acid is synthesized from urea and other wastes and is a mild irritant.

Muriatic acid, diluted hydrochloric acid, is used to lower the water's pH when it gets too high, which interferes with disinfection.

Sodium bisulfate is a dry acid alternative to muriatic acid.

Sodium carbonate is used to raise the water's pH when it's too low, which causes chlorine to dissipate too quickly.

Algaecides often contain copper, which is responsible for turning blond hair green.

Pool chemical safety

Most accidental exposures to pool chemicals are minimally toxic, but chemical reactions within and between products can have serious consequences.

Never mix pool chemicals. Contact between stabilized chlorine products (Dichlor and Trichlor) and calcium hypochlorite, for example, can be **explosive**. Keep them well separated.

Keep pool chemicals dry. Chlorine products are useful for sanitation when relatively small amounts are added to water. When a small amount of liquid leaks onto dry product, however, an **exothermic** (heat producing) reaction can occur resulting in **fire** or release of **toxic gases**.

Keep pool chemicals away from combustible materials like gasoline and paint thinner, as well as ignition sources like cars and lawn mowers. Chlorine isn't flammable but it's a vigorous oxidizer and can set off chemicals that are flammable.

What's that smell?

Urea is a nitrogen-containing metabolic byproduct excreted in urine and sweat. When urea enters chlorinated pool water, some of its nitrogen atoms are replaced with chlorine. The new compounds formed from chlorinated urea are called **chloramines**, which form a cloud of chloramine gas over the pool.

A properly chlorinated pool has little if any chlorine odor. A strong chlorine smell coming from a pool is actually due to high levels of chloramines, and indicates not that there is too much chlorine in the pool but that there is not enough.

Rubbing alcohol

How toxic: Minimally toxic to toxic

Mouth	**Skin**	**Eyes**	**Inhalation**
Toxic in large ingestions	*Extensive exposure may be toxic*	*May be irritating*	*Extensive exposure may be toxic*
▼	▼	▼	
Rinse mouth	Wash affected area	Irrigate	

What to expect

Rubbing alcohols can be intoxicating, so bitterants are added to make them hard to drink. Isopropyl alcohol can also be toxic with significant skin and inhalation exposures.

Symptoms after exposure to rubbing alcohol by any route require immediate medical care. Applying rubbing alcohol to a newborn's umbilical stump is unnecessary but not toxic.

Warning

Never use isopropyl alcohol to sponge bathe a feverish child; used this way it may be toxic both by inhalation and by absorption through the skin. Significant ingestion of rubbing alcohol is unlikely but not impossible. Headache, nausea, vomiting, mental status changes and breathing problems may occur early on; organ failure and death may follow.

Common ingredients

There are two kinds of rubbing alcohol: One is made with isopropyl alcohol and the other with ethanol. Despite the name neither is safe or effective for rubbing skin or massaging muscles, although both are effective antiseptics.

Isopropyl alcohol, also called **isopropanol**, is refined from fossil fuels such as petroleum, natural gas and coal. It is an effective solvent and has many industrial uses, but its solvent property means it can strip the natural oils from skin.

Isopropyl alcohol sold for home use is usually diluted with water to a concentration of about 60% to 70%, but it is available in concentrations up to 99%. HIgher concentrations are more effective at killing bacteria and viruses, but they are also more flammable and have a greater potential for toxicity.

Some adults have been known to drink isopropyl alcohol because it is cheap, readily available and highly intoxicating. It also has a strong, noxious odor and taste, which makes it unlikely anyone in your home who mistakes it for water will accidentally take more than one swallow before realizing their mistake.

Ethanol, or **ethyl alcohol**, is the same alcohol found in beer, wine and liquor. Ethanol rubbing alcohol is denatured by adding noxious chemicals to make it undrinkable. Again, it is very unlikely anyone in your home will get more than a taste by accident.

Sucrose octaacetate is made by chemically altering sucrose (cane or beet sugar) to make it extremely bitter. It is also found in the roots of some flowering plants of the *Clematis* genus. When ingested sucrose octaacetate is metabolized to sucrose and acetic acid and so is considered non-toxic; it is approved as a food additive although unlikely to be used for that purpose.

Methyl isobutyl ketone is synthesized from **acetone**. It has a number of industrial uses as well as being used to deter ingestion of rubbing alcohol.

Denatonium benzoate (p. 143) is a bittering agent used to prevent ingestion of many products that could be toxic.

 Other uses for isopropyl alcohol

Removing ink and permanent marker

Isopropyl alcohol may be effective in removing ballpoint pen ink and even permanent marker ink from fabrics and hard surfaces. For fabric, apply the alcohol to an absorbent cloth and dab the ink until the cloth comes away clean, then rinse the alcohol out and launder as usual. For a hard surface, apply the alcohol to a cloth and rub.

Household cleaning

Isopropyl alcohol dissolves oils well and dries quickly, making it an effective cleaning fluid for a wide variety of surfaces such as glass, stainless steel, and kitchen counters and appliances. It can be used to wipe accumulated oils from computer keyboards and cell phones.

Windshield de-icer

Mix 1 part water to 2 parts 70% isopropyl alcohol. Spray on ice to start it melting and then scrape off.

Sticker removal

Saturate stickers and let sit for a few minutes to dissolve the adhesive, then remove.

Fix powdered makeup that has cracked

Place broken pieces of eyeshadow, blush or foundation in a clean bowl and press with a spoon to a uniform powder. Add enough isopropyl alcohol to form a paste and put mixture back into palette; allow to dry.

Silica gel
How toxic: Not toxic

Mouth	**Skin**	**Eyes**	**Inhalation**
Not toxic	*Not toxic*	*Not expected*	*Not expected*
▼			
Rinse mouth			

What to expect

Silica gel is enticing to children because it comes in little packets that could be candy, although it is much too hard to be chewed.

It is no more toxic than sand and ingestion does not require medical attention or treatment.

Common ingredients

Silica gel is not toxic. Packets are marked "do not eat" because they could be mistaken for something edible, like candy. Silica gel passes through the body unchanged.

Silica gel is a synthetic form of **silicon dioxide**, found in nature as **quartz**. (Gemstones such as amethyst and citrine are varieties of quartz, and beach sand is often composed largely of silica.) The little packet of silica gel found in shoe boxes (among other products) contain small hard spheres, but before they take that form they actually are made into a liquid by melting **silica sand** and **soda ash** together.

The liquid form is **sodium silicate**, also known as **water glass**, and is used in many consumer products and industrial processes. Treating sodium silicate with an acid forms the beads we know as silica gel.

Silica gel beads are tunneled through with microscopic pores that increase their total surface area to unimaginable proportions: A teaspoon of silica gel beads has the surface area of an entire football field.

The beads can carry up to 40% of their own weight in water but because of their structure they never feel wet. Water molecules only cling to the surface of the beads rather than being absorbed into them, and silica gel can be dried out and reused.

Cobalt chloride is not used in the packets included with household products, but may be added to silica gel that is used for industrial and scientific purposes. Cobalt chloride is blue when dry but when it adsorbs water its crystalline structure is altered and it appears pink. Cobalt chloride is toxic and is banned in the EU.

Methyl violet (known in another form as **gentian violet**, p. 100), is used in the same way as cobalt chloride; it turns from orange when dry to green when saturated. It is considered a less-toxic alternative.

Uses for silica gel packets

Wet cell phone Remove battery, SIM and SD cards and place phone in a bowl or bag filled with silica gel packets for 24 hours.

Razors and razor blades Store in a closed container of gel packets to retard dulling.

Important documents Add packets to file box, drawer or envelope to prevent moisture damage to paper.

Electronics Add packets to camera cases and hearing aid holders.

Gardening Store seed envelopes in a box with gel packets.

Tarnish protection Add packets to silver drawer and jewelry box.

How to dry silica packets for re-use

Silica gel will begin releasing the water molecules on its surface when heated to about 220 F, but the packet that holds the gel is likely to be damaged if heated above 250 F.

- » Spread the silica gel packets on a baking sheet.
- » Place in the oven as far from heating elements as possible.
- » Set the temperature to between 220 F and 250 F.
- » Allow to dry for at least two hours, up to 24 hours.

It is not safe to dry or re-use silica gel that has been contaminated with anything other than water.

Other common desiccants

Zeolites are porous aluminum silicate mineral compounds that form naturally in volcanic rock and alkaline sediment. Synthetic zeolite desiccants adsorb water the way silica gel does and are known as **molecular sieves** because their pores are designed to allow only molecules of certain sizes to pass through. The small canisters found in **pharmaceutical** bottles often contain zeolites in combination with silica gel and activated charcoal.

Iron powder packets found in some dehydrated products such as beef jerky and dog treats look like desiccants but are actually **oxygen absorbers**. The iron in the packets turns to rust, binding oxygen in the process. They are used to protect food products from oxidation and microbial growth. Care should be taken with these iron packets because while humans are unlikely to ingest them **dogs** (mostly small ones) have been poisoned by them. Iron is corrosive and if a dog vomits or acts sick after eating iron in any form immediate veterinary care is needed.

Activated charcoal (p. 15) is also not a desiccant as it adsorbs **odors** rather than moisture. It is often combined with desiccants.

Slug & snail killers

How toxic: Not toxic to toxic

Mouth	**Skin**	**Eyes**	**Inhalation**
Rarely toxic	*Not toxic*	*May be irritating*	*May be irritating*
▼	▼	▼	▼
Rinse mouth	Wash affected area	Irrigate	Fresh air

What to expect

Most slug and snail killers are possibly irritating but otherwise not toxic.

The exception is metaldehyde, a neurotoxin that is easily avoided.

Common ingredients

Most slug and snail killers are made from mineral compounds that occur naturally in soil and contain essential nutrients. Biological differences mean these products are toxic to mollusks but not mammals.

Iron phosphate is a compound of iron and phosphorus, which are essential nutrients naturally found in soil. It is used in nutritional supplements, but when ingested by slugs and snails it causes them to stop feeding so they die slowly of starvation and dehydration. Iron phosphate that is not consumed is eventually broken down and returned to the soil.

Sodium ferric EDTA Our blood is red because the hemoglobin that transports oxygen around our bodies contains iron. Mollusks, including snails and slugs, have blue blood because the **hemocyanin** that transports oxygen around their bodies contains copper, which turns blue when it binds with oxygen. Sodium ferric EDTA interferes with hemocyanin and deprives a mollusk of oxygen, but it doesn't interact with hemoglobin and so doesn't have this effect on us or our pets.

Sulfur is an abundant element that can be recovered from salt domes and petroleum. It's nearly ubiquitous as it occurs in so many compounds. Many biological processes release hydrogen sulfide, which lends its noxious odor to rotten eggs, flatulence and other smelly substances. Sulfur causes slugs and snails to stop feeding. It is of very low toxicity to mammals and is a natural component of soil.

Metaldehyde degrades rapidly into acetaldehyde, the same chemical that is responsible for alcoholic hangovers. It makes slugs and snails lethargic and causes them to produce so much mucus they dehydrate. Metaldehyde is a **neurotoxin** that readily crosses the blood–brain barrier, making it a danger to children and pets. It was once commonly used as solid fuel for camp stoves, but most of these now burn **hexamine** instead.

Alternatives methods of controlling slugs & snails

Slugs are notoriously difficult to eliminate, as they live underground and only a small proportion of the local population is feeding above ground at any given time. Snails don't go underground but they do hide in damp, dark places. Slug and snail baits and killers can help control them but should be used in conjunction with other measures.

Methods often recommended but seldom effective

Beer or water with yeast in it will attract slugs, but unless it's in an inescapable trap or deep enough to drown in they will drink it and move on.

Coffee grounds, egg shells, sand It is often said that substances with sharp edges will kill or repel slugs and snails, but many people don't find them effective.

Copper Theories are that either copper is toxic to slugs and snails or it conducts an electrical charge when in contact with their mucus. Neither theory holds up under scrutiny, though, and copper is not proven to help.

Methods known to be effective

Diatomaceous earth (DE) A thick line of DE around a plant will keep slugs and snails away as long as it's dry, but once it gets wet they will slither right over it. DE is not poisonous and sprinkling it around won't kill slugs or snails.

Ammonia Going out after dark, manually removing slugs and placing them in a bucket of ammonia water is highly effective, although tedious and not for the squeamish.

Garlic Extract of garlic oil sprayed on soil will repel and kill slugs and snails and their eggs. It isn't known how it works but it may affect the mollusks' nervous system. Garlic **spray** can be made by boiling crushed garlic cloves in water. After straining and cooling, the water can be sprayed directly on plants.

Shelter Lay down boards or short pieces of garden hose for slugs and snails to shelter during the day. Turn over the boards or up-end the hose and remove any that you find.

Electrified wire Wrap the wood frame of a raised bed with two parallel lengths of stainless steel tie wire about ½ inch apart, leaving several extra inches on each end. Staple in place. Twist the ends of one length together and attach to one node of a 9 volt battery. Twist the ends of the other length together and attach them to the other node. Place the battery assembly in a plastic lidded container. Touching both wires at the same time as it climbs the frame gives the slug or snail a shock that will repel but not kill.

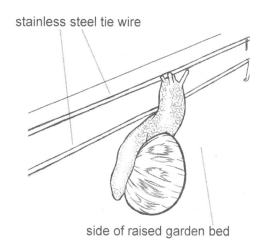

stainless steel tie wire

side of raised garden bed

Soaps & washes

How toxic: Not toxic to minimally toxic

Mouth	Skin	Eyes	Inhalation
May cause vomiting	*Not toxic*	*May be irritating*	*Not expected*
▼	▼	▼	
Rinse mouth, dilute	Wash affected area	Irrigate	

What to expect

Soaps are generally non-toxic but a good swallow may irritate the stomach and cause mild, limited vomiting.

A little plain water to dilute any soap that makes it to the stomach is all that is needed.

See laundry detergents, page 126, for information on **surfactants**.

Animal and vegetable fats are made of **triglycerides**, which have three fatty acids bound to glycerol (glycerin). Treating triglycerides with a strong alkali separates the fatty acids from the glycerol in a process called **saponification**. The fatty acids combine to form soap; the glycerol can be kept in to make the soap softer, or taken out for other uses. The alkali is not present in the finished product.

Soap was made for thousands of years by boiling animal fats in water with wood ash or potash, which are highly alkaline. This kind of soap was used for textiles and household cleaning. In time vegetable oils, especially olive oil, were substituted for animal fat, producing milder soaps.

About antibacterial soap

All soaps are antibacterial, as the process of washing with anything removes microbes from the skin. **Triclosan**, once the most common added antibacterial, was introduced for hospital use about 50 years ago and was added to consumer products shortly afterward. Research into whether antibacterials are hazardous to health or the environment, or whether they can cause bacteria to become antibiotic-resistant, have been inconclusive. But there's no evidence they prevent illness or have any other benefits, and in 2017 the FDA banned triclosan and 18 other antibacterials from household products.

Making your own soap

The process of making soap is too complicated to go into here, but recipes and instructions are readily available online and in books. A number of different oils can be used. Sodium hydroxide (lye) is used to make bar soap and potassium hydroxide is used to make liquid soap; both are easily obtained and both must be handled with care as they are extremely caustic.

soap (n.)

Old English *sape* "soap, salve" (originally a reddish hair dye used
by Germanic warriors to give a frightening appearance), from Proto-
Germanic *saipon* "dripping thing, resin" (source also of Middle Low
German *sepe*, West Frisian *sjippe*, Dutch *zeep*, Old High German *seiffa*,
German *seife* "soap," Old High German *seifar* "foam," Old English *sipian*
"to drip"), from PIE *soi-bon-*, from root *seib-* "to pour out, drip, trickle"
(source also of Latin *sebum* "tallow, suet, grease").

Romans and Greeks used oil to clean skin; the Romance words for "soap"
(Italian *sapone*, French *savon*, Spanish *jabon*) are from Late Latin *sapo*
"pomade for coloring the hair" (first mentioned in Pliny), which is a
Germanic loan-word, as is Finnish *saippua*. The meaning "flattery" is
recorded from 1853.

– Online Etymology Dictionary

Sunscreens

How toxic: Not toxic

Mouth	**Skin**	**Eyes**	**Inhalation**
Not toxic	*Sensitivity reaction possible*	*May be irritating*	*Not expected*
▼	▼	▼	
Rinse mouth	Wash affected area	Irrigate	

What to expect

Accidental ingestions of sunscreens are not toxic and no problems are expected.

Some common ingredients may cause allergic dermatitis with normal use.

Common ingredients

Sunscreens that use zinc and titanium oxides to block UV rays are called **physical** sunscreens. Products that convert UV rays to heat are called **chemical** sunscreens.

Oxybenzone is a highly effective broad spectrum UV blocker that is widely used not just in sunscreens but in many consumer products and in plastics to protect them from light degradation.

Unfortunately it has been shown to endanger **coral** by damaging its DNA; in small amounts it's fatal to baby coral and in larger amounts also affects adult coral. At the time of this writing oxybenzone-containing sunscreens have been banned in Hawaii and it is likely the ban will be more widespread in the future.

Homosalate is derived from salicylic acid, making it a cousin to aspirin. It protects against UVB radiation but is not photostable and doesn't offer much in the way of UVA protection, so it is always combined with other sunscreens. Homosalate is widely used and has a good safety profile; small amounts may be absorbed through the

skin and some studies have suggested it could be an endocrine disruptor, but so far it hasn't been shown to have this kind of effect.

Avobenzone is a popular broad spectrum UV blocker that is not very photostable, so it is blended with other ingredients that help stabilize it. Allergic dermatitis has been reported, but it is just as likely the sensitivity is due to the other ingredients. Sunlight and chlorine cause avobenzone to break down into other chemicals that, while they have not been proven problematic themselves, are of a type known to be toxic to the environment.

Octisalate is another salicylic acid derivative. Like homosalate it protects against UVB radiation only. The amounts absorbed through the skin have been shown to be minute and no ill effects are associated with octisalate use.

Octocrylene has modest UV blocking abilities but is used in combination with more effective sunscreens because it also moisturizes skin and helps stabilize and emulsify the other ingredients. It enhances absorption of chemical sunscreens so they work better, but there is some concern it can generate free radicals that can damage skin cells' DNA. It has also been implicated in increasing cases of allergic dermatitis.

Ecamsule (terephthalylidene dicamphor sulfonic acid) is a chemical sunscreen that is photostable and very effective but blocks a somewhat limited UV range and so is combined with other sunscreens for broad spectrum protection. It has been widely used for decades in Canada, Europe and elsewhere but despite no known safety concerns ecamsule is currently only approved for a very limited number of products in the US.

Enzacamene (4-methylbenzylidene camphor) is a chemical sunscreen that has been approved for use in Canada but not in the US. Studies have shown enzacamene is absorbed and shows up in blood and urine. While the amounts involved have not been proven to be unsafe, concerns about its possible status as an endocrine disruptor has kept it largely off the shelf.

How to use sunscreen

SPF stands for **sun protection factor**. A product with an SPF of 30 will block 97% of the sun's UV radiation, while SPF 50 will block 98%—if you use it correctly.

How often to apply

A good rule of thumb is to apply sunscreen 15 to 20 minutes before going out in the sun, again 15 to 20 minutes after being out, then every two hours and after sweating, swimming or rubbing the skin (such as by towel-drying). If your product says it's **water resistant** follow the label instructions for application.

How much to use

Apply one ounce of sunscreen (a shot glass worth) to cover all exposed skin. If only some skin is exposed, apply a teaspoonful to each body part (face, each arm, etc.).

Expiration dates

Sunscreen ingredients can degrade over time and become less effective. Discard and replace expired products. If you can't find an expiration date, toss any you've had for three years or more.

Alternatives to sunscreens

The importance of protection from UV radiation cannot be overstated. No matter what the internet says, **you can't make an effective sunscreen at home** (you can, however, make your own sunless tanning lotion; see p. 167). Zinc oxide is a very effective sunscreen, but it has to be evenly dispersed and maintained in suspension to provide safe UV protection, and this isn't something you can achieve in your home kitchen.

Additionally, many DIY sunscreen recipes are based on oils that actually magnify and intensify UV exposure. If you don't want to use a commercial product your only alternative is to **limit sun exposure**. Wear clothing and hats designed to block UV radiation. Stay in the shade. Avoid outdoor activities between 10:00 am and 4:00 pm, when radiation is most intense.

Sunless tanners

How toxic: Not toxic

Mouth	**Skin**	**Eyes**	**Inhalation**
Not toxic	*Sensitivity reaction possible*	*May be irritating*	*Not expected*
▼	▼	▼	
Rinse mouth	Wash affected area	Irrigate	

What to expect

Accidental ingestion of sunless tanners is not toxic. Sensitivity reactions with normal use are uncommon, although sensitivity to products with DHA has been reported.

Common ingredients

Sunless tanners for home use are made with the same basic ingredients as those used in tanning salons, although each product may have its own proprietary mix of vitamins, emollients and moisturizers.

Dihydroxyacetone (DHA) is a simple **sugar** that is usually produced by bacterial fermentation of **glycerin** (p. 108). It's also formed in our bodies during the process of breaking glucose down for fuel.

DHA reacts with amino acids in the **stratum corneum**, the outer layer of skin, to form brown pigments called **melanoidins**. It's not surprising that people sometimes complain their sunless tanner smells like burnt biscuits, because this browning is a **Maillard reaction** similar to the kind that colors breads and other cooked foods.

The stratum corneum is composed of dead skin cells and the brown color fades as the cells are shed. Little if any DHA applied to the skin penetrates further than these dead cells, but concerns have been raised that DHA **inhaled** during spray tanning has the potential to be carcinogenic.

It's also important to remember that sunless tanners don't provide protection against UV radiation (unless they have added sunscreen ingredients), and in fact skin may be more sensitive to sunlight for 24 hours after DHA is applied.

Keep in mind dihydroxyacetone (DHA) is not the same as **docosahexaenoic acid** (DHA), an omega-3 fatty acid taken orally as a dietary supplement. Cosmetic DHA is not approved for consumption, and dietary DHA does not affect skin color.

Erythrulose is a sugar found in red berries that works, like DHA, through a Maillard reaction. It is gentler on skin than DHA, producing a less pronounced color change that takes longer to develop. It is not used alone but is combined with DHA so its reddish hue can balance out DHA's more orange tone, and so its slower effect can help the color change last longer.

Bronzers and body makeup

Bronzers don't react with skin to build color; they coat the skin surface with colorants that easily wash off. They contain iron oxides that mimic the color of tanned skin, along with other minerals such as tin oxide and titanium oxide for opacity and mica for shimmer. They may also have blue and green dyes to counter the orange mineral tones.

Body makeup contains many of the same ingredients as bronzers but the primary purpose is to conceal freckles, veins and imperfections in skin. Like foundation for the face, body makeup washes off easily. The most popular products are made for legs but can be used all over.

Removing sunless tanner

Sunless tanners develop color over a period of hours and you can't always tell if you've applied it evenly or if you're going to like the final color. If you find you have streaks or blotches, or if the color is darker than you expected, there are some commonly recommended solutions.

» Exfoliate with a **baking soda and lemon juice paste** or **sugar scrub.**

» For large areas, slather on a thick coat of **baby oil**, wait 10 minutes and then shower off.

» **Whitening toothpaste** or **acetone nail polish remover** can be used on palms and between fingers.

 *Make your own sunless tanner*

DIY sunless tanners apply pigment on top of the skin rather than reacting with the skin. Pigment ingredients are mixed with lotion and smoothed on, or mixed with water and sprayed on.

Before using a sunless tanner of any kind you should always exfoliate well. There's no point in applying color to skin cells that are about to be shed; a good scrub gets you down to cells that will stick around for about 10 days.

Lotion tanners

To a mild, white lotion add one or more of the following:

» 100% pure **cocoa powder** (will wash off with next shower)

» Strong **tea** (cooled)

» Strong **coffee** (cooled)

Spray tanners

Fill a spray bottle with any of the following. Reapply each day until you get the color you want.

» Strong **tea** (cooled)

» Strong **coffee** (cooled)

» **Carrots** Cover 1 pound sliced, unpeeled carrots and 2 cups brown sugar with water; simmer for 3 hours and allow to cool, then strain.

Tea tree oil (Melaleuca alternifolia)

How toxic: Minimally toxic to toxic

Mouth	**Skin**	**Eyes**	**Inhalation**
May be toxic	*Sensitivity reactions may occur*	*May be irritating*	*Not expected*
▼	▼	▼	
Rinse mouth	Wash affected area	Irrigate	

What to expect

Tea tree oil can be toxic when swallowed. Vomiting, weakness, lack of coordination, drowsiness and coma have been reported.

Skin reactions are mild and uncommon. Tea tree oil degrades over time and sensitivity reactions are more likely when the oil is old.

Warning

Tea tree oil can be extremely toxic to cats and dogs. Never undiluted tea tree oil to treat your pet's flea bites or other skin conditions.

Tea tree oil is an essential oil extracted from *Melaleuca alternafolia*, a tree in the myrtle family that is native to **Australia**. Its common name is attributed to the 18th century British explorer James Cook, whose sailors made tea from its leaves.

Indigenous peoples in Australia have a long history of using tea tree leaves medicinally. Published reports in the 1920s touted its antimicrobial properties and its use spread throughout the country.

During WW II Australian soldiers are said to have carried tea tree oil in their kits, making knowledge of its usefulness more widespread. It fell out of favor when antibiotics were introduced but became popular again as interest in "natural" products grew.

About **100 components** of tea tree oil have been identified and progress is being made in determining which have beneficial effects. Products containing the oil have been shown to be effective in treating **acne**, **dandruff**, **athlete's foot** and **lice**. Internal use is discouraged.

Its toxicity seems to be due to **terpenes**, which are hydrocarbons also present in turpentine, camphor and absinthe.

A taste of tea tree oil is unlikely to cause symptoms, but full swallows have caused illness in small children, and pets have been poisoned by having undiluted tea tree oil applied to their skin.

Tea tree oil oxidizes on exposure to light and air and degrades into substances that can reduce its effectiveness and increase its toxicity. It should be stored tightly capped in a dark, cool place and once opened should be **discarded after one year**.

Chemical composition of tea tree oil

Terpinen-4-ol	α-Terpineol
γ-Terpinene	Aromadendrene
α-Terpinene	δ-Cadinene
1,8-Cineole	Limonene
Terpinolene	Sabinene
ρ-Cymene	Globulol
α-Pinene	Viridiflorol

Teething gel (benzocaine)

How toxic: Not toxic except in rare cases

Mouth	**Skin**	**Eyes**	**Inhalation**
Not toxic for most but see below	*Not toxic*	*May be irritating*	*Not expected*
▼	▼	▼	
Rinse mouth	Wash affected area	Irrigate	

What to expect

Benzocaine does **not** paralyze the throat or make it hard to breathe or swallow. Ingestion of numbing gel usually causes no symptoms.

Methemoglobinemia (see below) is rare and usually not severe, but in some cases it has been life-threatening.

Warning
Seek medical care for anyone experiencing dizziness, fainting, shortness of breath, or a bluish skin color after exposure to benzocaine.

Common ingredients

In May 2018 the FDA required companies to stop marketing teething products containing benzocaine due to the risk of methemoglobinmia.

Benzocaine is one of several local anesthetics (including lidocaine and procaine, better known as Novocain) designed to share cocaine's numbing qualities without its toxicity. All interrupt transmission of nerve impulses and prevent them reaching pain centers in the brain.

In rare cases benzocaine can cause a medical condition called **methemoglobinemia** that temporarily reduces the amount of oxygen carried in the bloodstream. The most common symptom is a bluish cast to the skin, known as **cyanosis**. A person with cyanosis may feel fine, but more serious symptoms like dizziness, shortness of breath and fainting may occur. Get immediate medical attention if you or anyone in your family develops cyanosis or feels unwell after exposure to benzocaine.

Adults may develop methemoglobinemia after undergoing medical or dental treatments involving benzocaine, but young children have typically been exposed through the use of numbing gels while they are teething. **Benzocaine teething gels are no longer sold in the US** and you are encouraged to discard any you may have.

According to the American Academy of Pediatrics these gels are ineffective anyway, because teething babies drool so much the gels are washed right out of the mouth. The Academy recommends using gum massage or hard rubber teething rings instead.

Eugenol is derived primarily from clove oil but is also found in cinnamon, nutmeg and bay leaf. Cloves, the dried flower buds of the clove tree, were used for flavoring, fragrance and medicinal purposes for thousands of years before eugenol was isolated from them. Pure, undiluted clove oil can cause painful ulcers and should be used in the mouth with caution.

Menthol can be derived from mint leaves or produced synthetically. Research continues into just how menthol helps relieve pain, but it works at least in part as a counterirritant, stimulating receptors in the skin with sensations of cold or heat and blocking transmission of pain impulses.

Zinc chloride is an astringent that soothes mucus membranes and promotes healing. Zinc is an essential nutrient and zinc compounds have been used topically for thousands of years.

Benzalkonium chloride is an antimicrobial surfactant often used in hand sanitizers (p. 112) and many other medications and cosmetics. It is intended to keep mouth sores from getting infected.

Homeopathic products (p. 115) contain no active ingredients. Products labeled as containing **belladonna** (deadly nightshade) are no longer sold in the US due to concerns they may cause harm by actually containing belladonna.

 *Alternatives to teething gel*

Around the house

Finger Massage gums with a clean finger.

Washcloth Wet cloth with water or chamomile tea, chill or freeze and allow baby to chew.

Spoon Chill (do not freeze) a spoon and use it to gently apply pressure to gums.

Chilled fluids and foods Generally appropriate for babies six months and older. Foods can be soft, like applesauce, or hard, like carrots, but keep an eye on a baby with hard foods that can be choking hazards. Sippy cups can dispense soothing fluids and the mouthpiece itself can be safely chewed on.

Special purchases

Necklace Pendants with mouthable silicone shapes are made to look like jewelry and are worn by mom, so baby can chew while being held.

Teether May be wooden, silicone or rubber and solid or filled with water; all can be chilled. The water in a filled teether may or may not be sterile, so it's probably best to discard it if it starts leaking.

Pacifier Any will do, but some are made specifically for teething. Some can be filled at home with chilled fruit, which is dispensed in small, safe amounts.

OTC anti-inflammatory Ibuprofen, for example, is generally very safe and effective. Dosing for children six months and over is provided on the label, but you are advised to consult with your health care provider if your baby is younger than six months.

Thermometers (liquid in glass)

How toxic: Not toxic to toxic

Mouth	**Skin**	**Eyes**	**Inhalation**
Not toxic	*Not toxic*	*May be irritating*	*Vapors may be toxic*
▼	▼	▼	▼
Rinse mouth	Wash affected area	Irrigate	See below

What to expect

Mercury from old thermometers isn't toxic on the skin or in the mouth, but is very toxic when inhaled. Mercury should never be vacuumed as this disperses it into the air.

Mercury should never be heated as inhalation of mercury vapors can have severe consequences. Mercury thermometers are no longer sold for home use.

Warning

Mercury **vapors** are extremely toxic. If a thermometer breaks, clean it up promptly (instructions on opposite page) and contact your waste management company for instructions on disposal.

Mercury thermometers

Liquid in glass thermometers work because liquids expand as they heat up and contract as they cool down. **Mercury** was once widely used in thermometers because it expands and contracts at a very regular rate, but it's a known neurotoxin that becomes dangerous when released into air, water or soil. Mercury thermometers are being **phased out** worldwide.

If you have a mercury thermometer, seal it in a plastic container such as a drink bottle and call your **waste management company** or local **hazardous waste facility** to ask what to do with it. If your area doesn't have a fixed location for hazardous waste disposal it likely has periodic collection drives. In many states it's **illegal** to throw a mercury thermometer in the trash.

Non-mercury thermometers

Alcohol thermometers If the liquid in your thermometer is **red** or **blue**, it is a **spirit** or **alcohol** thermometer and most likely contains ethanol with dye added for visibility. It can be wiped up like any other liquid.

Galinstan thermometers If the liquid in your thermometer is **silver** but it is labeled **non-toxic** or **mercury-free**, and almost certainly if it **less than 15 years old**, it contains Galinstan.

Galinstan is a non-toxic alloy of the metals **gallium**, **indium** and **tin**. It doesn't bead like mercury and is easier to clean up; it washes off surfaces with soap and water and it's perfectly **safe to vacuum** after a spill.

The different forms of mercury

Elemental mercury is the only metal that is liquid at room temperature. It is not absorbed through the skin or GI tract and isn't toxic when touched or swallowed. Its vapors, however, are toxic. Inhaled mercury molecules pass through the lungs into the bloodstream and from there can be distributed throughout the body, including the brain. Elemental mercury gives off some vapor at room temperature, and if it is exposed to heat its vapors can become deadly.

Inorganic mercury compounds are formed when elemental mercury binds with other elements such as oxygen, chlorine and sulfur. These compounds can be absorbed through the skin and GI tract rather than by inhalation. They primarily affect the kidneys but are not neurotoxic as they don't cross the blood–brain barrier. Inorganic mercury compounds are used in some industrial processes and are seldom if ever found in the home.

Organic mercury compounds contain carbon. Certain bacteria in soil and water can convert elemental and inorganic forms of mercury into the highly neurotoxic organic compound **methylmercury**. Methylmercury accumulates in the body when ingested and moves up the food chain as smaller creatures are eaten by larger ones. Methylmercury crosses the blood–brain barrier and the **placenta** and is excreted in **breast milk**. Pregnant women and nursing moms especially should be very careful about eating large **predator fish species** such as tilefish, swordfish, shark and king mackerel.

 Cleaning up a broken mercury thermometer

If the silver liquid from the thermometer smears rather than beading up, it's non-toxic Galinstan rather than mercury. If it breaks into little beads it's mercury, and it should be cleaned with care.

» Remove children and pets from the area.

» Pick up broken glass carefully and place on a paper towel. Fold the paper towel and place in a ziplock bag.

» Locate visible mercury beads. Hold a flashlight at a low angle to the floor in a darkened room and look for additional glistening beads of mercury that may be sticking to the surface or in small cracked areas of the surface. Be sure to search the entire room.

» Mercury beads can be scooped onto a piece of cardboard, drawn up with an eyedropper or collected with duct tape. Tape also helps pick up small glass fragments.

» Place all cleanup materials in a ziplock bag.

» Contact your local health department, municipal waste authority or your local fire department for proper disposal in accordance with local, state and federal laws.

» Keep the area well ventilated to the outside (windows open and fans in exterior windows running) and keep pets and children out of the cleanup area for at least 24 hours.

Toilet bowl cleaners

How toxic: Minimally toxic to toxic

Mouth	**Skin**	**Eyes**	**Inhalation**
May be irritating	*May be irritating*	*May cause injury*	*May be irritating if mixed with bleach*
▼	▼	▼	▼
Rinse mouth	Wash affected area	Irrigate for 30 minutes	Fresh air

What to expect

Liquid and gel toilet bowl cleaners may be either extremely acidic or extremely alkaline. Serious injury is very uncommon but not impossible; eyes require special care.

Any symptoms that persist after decontamination, especially involving the eyes, require immediate medical evaluation. Mixing with bleach causes noxious fumes.

Common ingredients

Toilet bowl cleaners are designed not just for surface cleaning but also for bleaching or removing limescale, which can become discolored, and for disinfecting bacteria that produce noxious smells.

Sodium hydroxide is also known as **lye**. It is highly alkaline and breaks the molecular bonds that hold fats and proteins together, turning them to a soapy liquid that is easily rinsed away.

Potassium hydroxide, also known as **potash**, is an alkaline very similar in structure and function to sodium hydroxide. It needs less water added to keep it liquid, though, and so products containing it can be more highly concentrated.

Sodium hypochlorite is the same chlorine compound found in liquid **bleach** (p. 42). It is antimicrobial and can bleach (but not remove) discolored limescale, which is formed when minerals in hard water accumulate.

Hydrochloric acid, sometimes called **muriatic acid**, is the same acid we have in our stomachs. In addition to its antimicrobial properties hydrochloric acid also dissolves limescale.

Quaternary ammonium compounds serve both as cationic (positively charged) surfactants that loosen soil and as disinfectants. They are widely used in part because they work very well with other surfactants and ingredients.

L-lactic acid is produced by *lactobaccilus* bacteria and has long been used in food fermentation, in part because of its antibacterial properties. Surfactants in a cleaning product weaken bacterial cell walls, allowing lactic acid to move in for the kill.

Automatic toilet bowl cleaners

In the 1980s a man with a swimming pool got the idea to weigh down a cup of chlorine with rocks and put it in his toilet tank. Pleased with the way it kept his toilet bowl clean, he went on to invent 2000 Flushes® and create a market for in-the-tank automatic toilet bowl cleaners.

The popularity of these products led to an epidemic of **leaky flappers** (the part that plugs the hole in the bottom of the tank after flushing) because the cleaning chemicals ate away at flapper edges.

Automatic cleaners that hang over the rim of the bowl don't have the same problem because they don't come in contact with the hardware in the tank.

Flappers are now made to withstand the corrosive effects of soaking in automatic bowl cleaner chemicals, as long as the toilet is flushed at least once a day. It's best not to toss a tablet in before leaving on vacation.

Solid toilet bowl cleaners

Tablets are not toxic while they are dry, but their ingredients are designed to be activated in the presence of water. Handling a wet tablet or putting one in a wet mouth can be irritating.

Toilet bowl cleaning wands have the same kind of ingredients as other products, just embedded in some kind of fiber. They are not more toxic but do pose a potential choking hazard.

 Make your own toilet bowl cleaner

Vinegar

Pour ½ cup distilled white vinegar into the bowl and leave for 5 minutes. Scrub with toilet bowl brush and flush.

Borax

To remove limescale, add ⅓ to ½ cup borax to the bowl and leave for anywhere from a few minutes to overnight. Scrub and flush. For severe limescale buildup you may need to drain the water from the bowl and scrub with a borax and vinegar paste.

Toilet bowl bombs

1 part baking soda
1 part citric acid
1 part borax (optional)

To use, drop a bomb into the toilet bowl and wait until it stops fizzing; scrub with brush if needed and then flush.

» Mix equal parts **baking soda** and **citric acid** with enough water to make a stiff paste. For limescale, add an equal part **borax** as well. Essential oils are optional.

» Roll paste into balls, scoop with a spoon, or press into an ice cube tray.

» Allow to dry, then unmold and leave until hard enough to handle. Store in an airtight container.

Urine

How toxic: Not toxic

Mouth	**Skin**	**Eyes**	**Inhalation**
Not toxic	*Not toxic*	*May be irritating*	*Not expected*
▼	▼	▼	
Rinse mouth	Wash affected area	Irrigate	

What to expect

Urine is harder to access than feces and ingestion is much less likely, but it isn't unheard of.

No symptoms are expected with an accidental or exploratory ingestion but check in with a healthcare provider for any concerns.

The production of **urine** is the end result of a complex process for balancing fluids and electrolytes in the body, as well as removing waste products. The average daily urine output for an adult human is 1.4 L, but the amount produced varies according to fluid intake and overall health.

Urine is about 95% **water**, with the remainder a complex mixture of **urea**, **creatinine**, **uric acid**, **enzymes**, **carbohydrates**, **hormones** and **electrolytes** such as sodium, calcium and potassium. Over a period of 24 hours you excrete about **59 g** of these substances. A dollar bill weighs 1 g, so the weight of the solids you urinate in a day is equivalent to about 59 dollar bills.

Bladder capacity depends on age. Infants up to one year can hold, in milliliters, seven times their weight in kilograms. Older children can hold, in ounces, their weight in years of age +2. Adults have a wide range, 300 ml to 600 ml. A cat's bladder holds 150 ml to 250 ml. Dogs make 2 ml of urine per kilogram of body weight per hour.

Urine color

Urine is yellow due to **urochrome**, also known as **urobilin**, released during further breakdown of the **bilirubin** that makes feces brown. Normal urine is pale to medium yellow; dark urine is usually due to dehydration. Persistently dark or discolored urine may indicate a medical problem and requires medical attention.

Foods that affect urine color

Bright yellow
Water-soluble B vitamins

Red, pink, orange
Beets, rhubarb, blackberries

Blue or green
Sweet snacks and drinks, green beer
Asparagus

Brown
Fava beans, rhubarb, aloe

FALSTAFF

What says the doctor of my water?

PAGE

He says the water is good healthy water, but the party that made it might have more diseases than he knows of.

– William Shakespeare, *Henry IV*

Washing soda (sodium carbonate)

How toxic: Minimally toxic to toxic

Mouth	**Skin**	**Eyes**	**Inhalation**
May be irritating	*May be irritating with extended use*	*May be irritating*	*May be irritating*
▼	▼	▼	▼
Rinse mouth	Wash affected area	Irrigate	Fresh air

What to expect

Usually irritating to skin only with lengthy exposure. May cause burns to mouth, eyes and respiratory tract. Get immediate medical attention for drooling, difficulty swallowing, coughing or changes to breathing after ingestion or inhalation. Any discomfort or vision change that persists after irrigation requires medical evaluation.

Sodium carbonate alkalizes wash water, increasing the number of negatively charged ions. Because soil and fabric fibers both tend to have negative charges, adding more negative ions to the water increases the repellent forces between them. Sodium carbonate also binds the minerals (mostly calcium and magnesium) in hard water that reduce detergent effectiveness.

Sodium carbonate and its near relative **sodium bicarbonate** (baking soda) are derived from a sodium compound called **trona**. In 1938 a large deposit of trona was discovered in Sweetwater County, Wyoming.

Today this deposit—which began accumulating 50 to 60 million years ago at the site of an ancient lake—provides about 90% of domestic production and about one-third of global production of sodium carbonate. It's expected to continue producing at this level for thousands of years.

About half the sodium carbonate, also known as **soda ash**, mined in Wyoming is used for glassmaking. The rest is used in the manufacture of other chemicals and numerous consumer products. While it isn't safe to ingest straight up, it is safely incorporated into medications and foods.

How to make washing soda from baking soda

Making your own washing soda won't save you money over just buying it, but it's a fun chemistry experiment and may be useful if you live in an area where washing soda isn't carried in stores.

To make washing soda, spread baking soda in a shallow pan and bake in a 400 degree oven for an hour. The baking soda ($NaHCO_3$) gives off water (H_2O) and carbon dioxide (CO_2), leaving behind the washing soda (Na_2CO_3).

 *Uses for washing soda*

Laundry booster Add ½ cup to regular loads, and 1 cup for heavily soiled loads or if you have hard water.

Pretreat stains Make a paste of 3 parts washing soda to 1 part water. Rub gently on the stain and launder as usual.

Cleaning Washing soda's alkalinity makes it an excellent solvent. Add ½ cup washing soda to one gallon warm water for an all-purpose degreasing cleaner. Do not use on fiberglass or aluminum.

Oil on concrete Pour over the oil and add water until a paste forms. Leave overnight, then scrub with a brush and rinse.

Tarnished silver Silver picks up sulfur from the air and forms silver sulfide, which is black. Sulfur prefers aluminum, though, and with a boost from salt and washing soda sulfur atoms will happily abandon silver for aluminum foil.

Line a plastic or glass dish with foil, shiny side up. Pour in enough hot water to cover items to be cleaned and add some salt and washing soda (exact amounts are not important.)

Lay tarnished items in the dish so they are fully immersed and at least part of each one is touching the foil. Let sit for about five minutes, then rinse well and dry with a soft cloth.

Repeat the process if any tarnish remains.

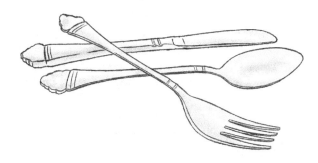

Witch hazel

How toxic: Not toxic to minimally toxic

Mouth	**Skin**	**Eyes**	**Inhalation**
May contain alcohol	*May be irritating*	*May be irritating*	*Not expected*
▼	▼	▼	
Rinse mouth	Wash affected area	Irrigate	

What to expect

Witch hazel USP is 14% ethanol and a significant ingestion could cause intoxication, although this is not likely to occur.

Some ingredients added to alcohol-free products can irritate the skin of sensitive individuals.

Common ingredients

The ethanol in witch hazel is both an astringent and a preservative.
Alcohol-free products have other preservatives added.

Witch hazel is distilled from the bark of the *Hamamelis virginiana* shrub. Native Americans have used witch hazel for hundreds of years, both internally and externally, for a variety of ailments. It was first commercialized in the 1840s as **Pond's Extract**, first as a patent medicine cure-all and then as an antiseptic.

Witch hazel grows in much of the US and is used as an ornamental in home gardens, valued because it flowers in winter. Most witch hazel products sold in the US are made from shrubs growing wild on private land in Connecticut.

Witch hazel USP as approved by the FDA is 86% witch hazel distilled from the **bark and twigs** of *Hamamelis virginiana* and 14% ethanol. **Witch hazel INCI** is distilled from the **leaves**. Much of witch hazel's usefulness in reducing inflammation is due to its **astringency**, or ability to make tissues contract. The **tannins** that make it an astringent are lost in distillation, though, and it's the ethanol that puts the bite back in. An alternative to distilling witch hazel is preparing a **decoction** (see next page), which retains the natural tannins.

Citric acid may be used as a preservative in alcohol-free products. Found in citrus fruits like lemons, limes and oranges, citric acid also plays a vital energy-producing role in our own bodies. Until the early 19th century most of the world's citric acid was produced in Italy from fresh fruit, but most is now produced through fermentation of yeasts and molds.

Grapefruit seed extract (GSE) is purported to have antimicrobial properties, but studies have shown that is only true when it is contaminated with synthetic preservatives such as benzalkonium chloride, triclosan and methylparaben. Unadulterated GSE has not been shown to have any antimicrobial effect.

Phenoxyethanol is a widely used preservative that may cause skin sensitivity reactions for some. It can be neurotoxic when ingested in sufficient quantities, but as with most household product ingredients, it is not likely anyone in your home will drink enough alcohol-free witch hazel to have a problem with it.

Suggested uses

Facial toner Splash or apply with a cotton ball to tighten pores and calm irritated skin.

Sunburn Apply witch hazel compresses to ease heat and redness.

Hemorrhoids Apply to anal area with a cotton ball or pad to reduce itching and swelling.

Eczema Witch hazel ointments are available that help with itching, swelling and peeling.

 Make your own witch hazel decoction or tincture

You can buy witch hazel bark online, or try gathering your own. Keep in mind *Hamamelis virginiana* is the only shrub of this family used for medicinal purposes. It is very slow growing and must be harvested with great care to avoid damaging the shrub.

Decoction

» Place bark in a stainless steel pot and cover with distilled water.

» Bring to a boil, reduce heat and simmer, covered, for 30 minutes.

» Allow to cool and strain into a glass container. Refrigerate and use within one week.

» To make the decoction last longer, measure the amount of liquid you end up with and add 20% unflavored vodka (for example, if you have 5 ounces of liquid, add 1 ounce vodka).

Tincture

» Place bark in a glass jar and cover with unflavored vodka.

» Store in in a cool, dark place for 6 weeks, then strain.

» To use, add 1 tablespoon tincture to 4 ounces distilled water.

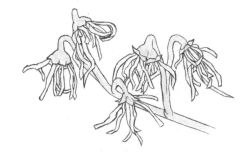

witch hazel blossoms

Index

9 78